For Reference

Not to be taken from this room

88th Congress, 2d Session

House Document Number 362

Compilation of Works of Art and Other Objects in the United States Capitol

For sale by the Superintendent of Documents, U.S. Government Printing Office
Washington, D.C., 20402 – Price $4.50

UNITED STATES CAPITOL, East Front

88th Congress, 2d Session

House Document Number 362

Compilation of Works of Art
and Other Objects in the
United States Capitol

PREPARED BY THE ARCHITECT OF THE CAPITOL UNDER THE
DIRECTION OF THE JOINT COMMITTEE ON THE LIBRARY

UNITED STATES
GOVERNMENT PRINTING OFFICE
WASHINGTON
1965

COMMITTEE ON HOUSE ADMINISTRATION

Eighty-ninth Congress—First Session

OMAR BURLESON, Texas, *Vice Chairman*

SAMUEL N. FRIEDEL, Maryland
ROBERT T. ASHMORE, South Carolina
WAYNE L. HAYS, Ohio
PAUL C. JONES, Missouri
FRANK THOMPSON, JR., New Jersey
WATKINS, M. ABBITT, Virginia
JOE D. WAGGONNER, JR., Louisiana
CARL D. PERKINS, Kentucky
JOHN H. DENT, Pennsylvania
SAM M. GIBBONS, Florida
LUCIEN N. NEDZI, Michigan
JOHN BRADEMAS, Indiana
JOHN W. DAVIS, Georgia
KENNETH J. GRAY, Illinois
AUGUSTUS F. HAWKINS, California
JONATHAN B. BINGHAM, New York

GLENARD, P. LIPSCOMB, California
ROBERT J. CORBETT, Pennsylvania
CHARLES, E. CHAMBERLAIN, Michigan
CHARLES E. GOODELL, New York
WILLARD S. CURTIN, Pennsylvania
SAMUEL L. DEVINE, Ohio
JOHN N. ERLENBORN, Illinois
WILLIAM L. DICKINSON, Alabama

JULIAN P. LANGSTON, *Chief Clerk*

JOINT COMMITTEE ON THE LIBRARY

Eighty-ninth Congress—First Session

OMAR BURLESON, Representative from Texas, *Chairman*
B. EVERETT JORDAN, Senator from North Carolina, *Vice Chairman*

CLAIBORNE PELL
Senator from Rhode Island

JOSEPH S. CLARK
Senator from Pennsylvania

PAUL C. JONES
Representative from Missouri

FRANK THOMPSON, JR.
Representative from New Jersey

JOHN SHERMAN COOPER
Senator from Kentucky

HUGH SCOTT
Senator from Pennsylvania

GLENARD P. LIPSCOMB
Representative from California

ROBERT J. CORBETT
Representative from Pennsylvania

JULIAN P. LANGSTON, *Chief Clerk*
GORDON F. HARRISON, *Assistant Chief Clerk*
(Prepared under the direction of the Eighty-eighth and Eighty-ninth Congresses)

Foreword

The accumulation of the works of art in the United States Capitol represents a paramount and most interesting portion of the history of this great edifice, which, since the laying of its cornerstone in 1793 by President George Washington, has developed into one of our most cherished and revered national shrines. The collection has grown in numbers, value, and reputation and has become an integral part of this world-famed structure.

From the time the first work of art was placed in the Capitol until 1927, there were only occasional compilations made, none of which followed any definite pattern, or standard, and most of which contained only general, incomplete, and oftentimes unsubstantiated information. Thirty-eight years ago, in 1927, Charles E. Fairman, then art curator of the Capitol, compiled the most comprehensive history of the accumulation and development of art in the Capitol ever prepared. This voluminous work, undoubtedly, is the most valuable writing presently available concerning this particular subject matter. Its historical and encyclopedical usefulness cannot be overestimated.

By 1952 it had been apparent for some time, nevertheless, that a simple, concise, comprehensive, and factual cataloging of these works of art had been long overdue. Fairman's "Art and Artists" was by then approximately a quarter of a century out of date; it is narrative in form; it was written primarily from an artist's perspective; and, consequently, it does not contain certain factual information which, though unimportant to the artist or art critic, is most important to the cataloger.

The impelling need in 1952 for a current official cataloging culminated in the Architect of the Capitol compiling in concise form a complete list of all the art in the Capitol, together with the date and manner of acquisition, the location of each and the names of the respective painters and sculptors. The members of the Joint Committee on the Library were greatly impressed by the thoroughness of that compilation and, in the interest of both Houses of Congress, decided to have it printed as a joint committee print.

Since 1952 a number of works of art, particularly statues in the Statuary Hall collection, have been added to the art collection of the United States Capitol. I introduced House Concurrent Resolution 350 in order to make available a complete and up-to-date compilation of works of art in the Capitol. The meticulous accumulation of facts, the graphic illustrations of the various objects of art, and the excellent grouping of related items are the result of painstaking efforts on the part of the Architect of the Capitol and his very able staff. Particular credit is due Mrs. Lillian Kessel, Administrative Assistant, who is principally responsible for the research and organization of this work, and to Mr. Harry L. Burnett, Jr., photographer for the architect, whose whose excellent work is self-evident. This publication includes numerous illustrations, a feature which will add greatly to the value of the work. It also includes a wider range of art works, such as the "Statue of Freedom," the "Bronze Doors," the statuary of the "Pediments," the "State Seals" in the Hall of the House, frescoes and murals, bas reliefs, mantels, the Rotunda frieze and fresco of the canopy, commemorative plaques and markers, and more extensive historical information.

The organization of this work is convenient in that it is divided into related areas, such as portraits, paintings, busts, etc. with complete indexing.

OMAR BURLESON, *Chairman*
Committee on House Administration

(Submitted by Mr. Burleson)

Eighty-eighth Congress of the United States of America

CONCURRENT RESOLUTION

Resolved by the House of Representatives (the Senate concurring), That there be printed with illustrations as a House document a "Compilation of Works of Art and Other Objects in the United States Capitol", prepared under the direction of the Architect of the Capitol; and that there be printed thirty-seven thousand two hundred and fifty additional copies of such document, of which ten thousand three hundred copies shall be for the use of the Senate, twenty-one thousand nine hundred and fifty copies shall be for the use of the House of Representatives, and five thousand for the use of the Architect of the Capitol.

Attest:

RALPH R. ROBERTS,
Clerk of the House of Representatives.

Attest:

FELTON M. JOHNSTON,
Secretary of the Senate.

Contents

List of Illustrations

39–071—65——2

The photographs reproduced in this book, with several exceptions, as noted, are the property of the U.S. Government, Office of the Architect of the Capitol, United States Capitol, Washington, D.C. Glossy prints (8″ x 10″) may be purchased by Title and Neg. No. from the Photoduplication Service, Library of Congress, Washington, D.C.

Included in This Book Are the Following Diagrams:

Jurisdiction Over Works of Art in the Capitol

Since 1872, the Joint Committee on the Library has had supervision of all works of art in the United States Capitol, under the provisions of section 1831 of the Revised Statutes of the United States as follows:

The Joint Committee on the Library, whenever, in their judgment, it is expedient, are authorized to accept any work of the fine arts, on behalf of Congress, which may be offered, and to assign the same such place in the Capitol as they may deem suitable, and shall have the supervision of all works of art that may be placed in the Capitol.

The Capitol Art Collection

COMPRISES A TOTAL OF 744 WORKS OF ART AND OTHER OBJECTS AS OF JUNE 1964

128 Portraits:

14 of Presidents of the United States.

2 of Vice Presidents of the United States.

44 of Speakers of the House of Representatives.

7 other small portraits of Speakers of the House of Representatives.

22 of United States Senators.

21 of chairmen of the House Committee on Appropriations.

7 of Architects of the Capitol.

11 of other prominent individuals.

54 Paintings: (OTHER THAN PORTRAITS)

8 large historical paintings in the Rotunda.

12 paintings, principally historic, in the Senate wing of the Capitol.

5 paintings, historic, in the House wing of the Capitol.

18 paintings in the Central section of the Capitol.

> 17 paintings of forts, representing the principal fortifications of the United States during the period of the 1870's; 1 painting of the United States Capitol, (watercolor).

10 paintings in the House Office Buildings.

> 9 paintings of Indian scenes, located in the Longworth House Office Building; 1 painting in the Cannon House Office Building.

1 painting in the Old Senate Office Building.

75 Marble and Bronze Busts:

7 of Presidents of the United States.

35 of Vice Presidents of the United States.

1 of President pro tempore of the Senate, Lafayette S. Foster.

10 of Chief Justices of the United States.

3 of United States Senators.

9 of Speakers and Members of the House of Representatives, located in the Rotunda of the Cannon House Office Building.

7 of international and other outstanding figures.

3 of Indian chief (2) and warrior (1).

95 Statues in the United States Capitol:

86 statues, contributed by States to the Statuary Hall Collection:

> 2 statues contributed by each of 39 States.
> 1 statue contributed by each of 8 States.
> Total: 45 marble, 41 bronze, of which 47 are located in Statuary Hall and 39 in other sections of the Capitol.

8 statues, not contributed by States:

> Jefferson (2), Franklin, Hancock, Hamilton, Lincoln, Baker and Grant.

1 plaster statue of Liberty and the Eagle in Statuary Hall.

1 Sculptured Marble Portrait Monument:

Portrait monument of Elizabeth Cady Stanton, Susan B. Anthony and Lucretia Mott, located in the Crypt of the Capitol.

23 Relief Portraits of Lawgivers:

23 relief portraits in marble over gallery doors, House Chamber: Portraits of men noted in history for the part played by them in the evolution of what has become American law.

67 Sculptured Reliefs:

52 State and other seals.

1 "Justice" located in the Supreme Court Chamber, First floor.

8 in the Rotunda.

3 in the Senate Chamber.

3 on the Portico.

165 *Frescoes, Murals and Lunettes:* (PARTIAL LISTING)

1 fresco, "Apotheosis of Washington," Canopy of the Dome.
1 Rotunda frieze.
93 in the Senate wing.
70 in the House wing.

120 *Miscellaneous Works of Art:* (INTERIOR)

14 mantels.
1 model of the United States Capitol.
5 mottoes in plaques or panels in the Capitol Building.
16 plaques and markers:

    13 plaques and markers in the Capitol Building.
    2 on the Capitol Grounds.
    1 transferred from the Capitol Grounds (stored).

1 Centennial Safe.
67 miscellaneous sculpture: Capitals, Clocks, Eagles—Statuary Hall and Old Supreme Court Chamber, Rinehart Fountain, Mary Washington Monument, Bronze Mask, Statuettes of Pericles and Phideas, Bronze Stairways, and Vases.
16 stained glass windows and skylights.

14 *Exterior Works of Art:*

7 statues: Freedom, Discovery Group, Rescue Group, War, Peace, Justice and History.
4 bronze doors: Central, House, Senate and West entrances.
3 pediment sculptures: Central, House and Senate.

2 *Monuments and Memorials on the Capitol Grounds:*

1 Marshall statue.
1 Taft Memorial.
744 Total Works of Art and other objects in the Capitol collection.

51 *Portraits, Paintings, Photographs and Busts:*
(PROPERTY OF HOUSE AND SENATE COMMITTEES)
1 bust.
2 paintings.

2 photographs tinted in oil.
46 portraits.

46 *Works of Art Transferred from the Capitol:*

3 busts: Supreme Court.
1 chandelier.
4 paintings.
32 portraits: Supreme Court and others.
5 statues: Freedom, Il Penseroso, Tecumseh, and Washington (2).
1 monument: Tripoli or Peace.

1,239 *Works of Art Lost in Fires:*

16 busts.
1200 medals.
20 portraits.
3 statues.

48 *Works of Art:* (NOT CARRIED IN THE RECORDS OF THE ARCHITECT OF THE CAPITOL AS A PART OF THE CAPITOL ART COLLECTION)

The Joint Committee on the Library has not acted towards acceptance of these works of art,— some gifts, some left by owners who cannot be located, some for which the records are incomplete and some works which cannot now be located.
5 busts.
1 painting.
20 portraits.
2 enlarged photographs tinted in oil.
1 colored lithograph.
1 statuette.
16 works of art on indefinite loan to Capitol:

    14 paintings.
    2 portraits.

1 painting—the property of Speaker of the House of Representatives, John McCormack.

3 *Paintings on Indefinite Loan to the Capitol and Returned.*

4 *Portraits Carried in 1952 Compilation as Works of Art Not Government Property.* (RETURNED TO OWNERS)

1,390 other works of art and objects.

Portraits Located in the United States Capitol

PRESIDENTS OF THE UNITED STATES
Fourteen Portraits

JOHN ADAMS, portrait by Eliphalet Frazer Andrews, acquired by purchase about 1882 (records incomplete), located in Senate wing, main corridor, second floor.

JAMES A. GARFIELD, mosaic portrait by Antonio Salviati, acquired as a gift from the artist about 1882, located in Senate wing, third floor, east.

ULYSSES S. GRANT, portrait by William Cogswell, acquired by purchase in 1886, located in Office of Senate Majority Leader, S–210.

ANDREW JACKSON, portrait by Thomas Sully, acquired by purchase in 1922, located in Senate wing, main corridor, second floor.

THOMAS JEFFERSON, portrait by Thomas Sully, acquired by purchase in 1874, located in Senate wing, main corridor, second floor.

ABRAHAM LINCOLN, mosaic portrait by Antonio Salviati, acquired by purchase in 1866, located in Senate wing, third floor, east.

ABRAHAM LINCOLN, portrait by Freeman Thorp, acquired by purchase in 1920, located in Senate wing, main corridor, second floor.

GEORGE WASHINGTON, portrait by William Dunlap, accepted by the Joint Committee on the Library as a gift from Mrs. A. V. H. Ellis in 1940, located in Office of Architect of the Capitol, Room SB–15.

GEORGE WASHINGTON, portrait by Charles Willson Peale, acquired by purchase in 1882, located in Senate wing, third floor, west side.

GEORGE WASHINGTON, portrait by Rembrandt Peale (the Porthole portrait), acquired by purchase in 1832. The portrait originally hung in the Old Senate Chamber, later the Old Supreme Court Room, S–228. In 1859 it was moved to its present location in the Vice President's formal office, Room S–214.

GEORGE WASHINGTON, portrait by Gilbert Stuart (the Thomas Chestnut portrait) acquired by purchase in 1876, located in Senate wing, main corridor, second floor.

GEORGE WASHINGTON, portrait by Gilbert Stuart (the Edward Pennington portrait) acquired by purchase in 1886, located in Office of Senate Majority Leader, Room S–210.

GEORGE WASHINGTON, portrait by Gilbert Stuart (the Lansdowne or Teapot type), was originally presented to the United States Embassy in Madrid, Spain, in 1818 by Richard Worsam Meade, of Philadelphia, Pennsylvania, a merchant and United States Naval agent in Cadiz, Spain. The portrait was transferred by the State Department from the Embassy to Washington, D.C., in July 1951 with the approval of the President of the United States. It was placed in Statuary Hall with the approval of the Speaker of the House of Representatives. In 1962 the portrait was moved to the House Reception Room, H–207, second floor, Capitol Extension, with the approval of the Speaker.

GEORGE WASHINGTON, portrait by John Vanderlyn, acquired by the House of Representatives in 1834, by purchase, under House resolutions of February 17, 1832, and June 27, 1834, located on south wall of House Chamber.

JOHN ADAMS
Portrait by Eliphalet Frazer Andrews.
Located in Senate wing, second floor, main corridor.

JAMES A. GARFIELD, Mosaic portrait.
Portrait by Antonio Salviati.
Located in Senate wing, third floor, east.

3

ULYSSES S. GRANT
Portrait by William Cogswell.
Location: Office of the Senate Majority Leader.

ANDREW JACKSON
Portrait by Thomas Sully.
Located in Senate wing, second floor, main corridor.

THOMAS JEFFERSON
Portrait by Thomas Sully.
Located in Senate wing, second floor, main corridor.

ABRAHAM LINCOLN, Mosaic portrait
Portrait by Antonio Salviati.
Located in Senate wing, third floor, east.

Neg. No. 23938

ABRAHAM LINCOLN
Portrait by Freeman Thorp.
Located in Senate wing, second floor, main corridor.

Neg. No. 23105

GEORGE WASHINGTON
Portrait by William Dunlap.
Location: Office of the Architect of the Capitol.

9

GEORGE WASHINGTON
Portrait by Charles Willson Peale.
Location: Senate wing, third floor, west side.

PATRIÆ PATER

GEORGE WASHINGTON (Porthole portrait)
Portrait by Rembrandt Peale.
Location: Formal Office of the Vice President.

GEORGE WASHINGTON (Thomas Chestnut portrait)
Portrait by Gilbert Stuart.
Location: Senate wing, second floor, main corridor.

GEORGE WASHINGTON (the Edward Pennington portrait)
Portrait by Gilbert Stuart.
Location: Office of Senate Majority Leader.

13

GEORGE WASHINGTON (Lansdowne portrait)
Portrait by Gilbert Stuart.
Location: House Reception Room.

GEORGE WASHINGTON
Portrait by John Vanderlyn.
Location: south wall of House Chamber.

VICE PRESIDENTS OF THE UNITED STATES

Two Portraits

JOHN C. CALHOUN, portrait by Henry F. Darby, acquired by purchase in 1881, located in Senate wing, main corridor, second floor.

JOHN NANCE GARNER, portrait by Howard Chandler Christy, acquired by purchase in 1940, under Public Law 723, Seventy-fifth Congress, located in Office of the Vice President, Room S–212.

Neg. No. 24313

Neg. No. 25975

JOHN C. CALHOUN
Portrait by Henry F. Darby.
Location: Senate wing, main corridor, second floor.

JOHN NANCE GARNER
Portrait by Howard Chandler Christy.
Location: Office of the Vice President.

SPEAKERS OF THE HOUSE OF REPRESENTATIVES
Forty-Four Portraits

This collection includes all Speakers of the House of Representatives from Speaker Muhlenberg of the First Congress through Speaker Rayburn of the Eighty-seventh Congress. Forty-three of these portraits are located in the Speaker's lobby and one (the portrait of Speaker Martin) is temporarily located in Mr. Martin's private office. A portrait of Speaker John W. McCormack has been authorized (Public Law 87–730), but not yet painted.

FREDERICK A. C. MUHLENBERG, Pennsylvania: Speaker, First and Third Congresses. Portrait by Samuel B. Waugh, from an early portrait by Joseph Wright.

JONATHAN TRUMBULL, Connecticut: Speaker, Second Congress. Portrait by H. I. Thompson.

JONATHAN DAYTON, New Jersey: Speaker, Fourth, and first session of Fifth, Congresses. Portrait by Henry Harrison.

THEODORE SEDGWICK, Massachusetts: Speaker, Sixth Congress. Portrait by Edgar Parker (copy of original by Gilbert Stuart).

NATHANIEL MACON, North Carolina: Speaker, Seventh, Eighth, and Ninth Congresses. Portrait by Robert D. Gauley.

JOSEPH B. VARNUM, Massachusetts: Speaker, Tenth and Eleventh Congresses. Portrait by Charles L. Elliott.

HENRY CLAY, Kentucky: Speaker, Twelfth and Thirteenth, second session Fourteenth, Fifteenth, first session Sixteenth, and Eighteenth Congresses. Portrait by Giuseppe Fagnani.

LANGDON CHEVES, South Carolina: Speaker, succeeded Henry Clay, second session Thirteenth Congress. Portrait by Hal Morrison.

JOHN W. TAYLOR, New York: Speaker, second session Sixteenth Congress, and Nineteenth Congress. Portrait by Miss C. L. O. Ransom.

PHILIP PENDLETON BARBOUR, Virginia: Speaker, Seventeenth Congress. Portrait by Kate Flournoy Edwards.

ANDREW STEVENSON, Virginia: Speaker, Twentieth, Twenty-first, Twenty-second, and first session Twenty-third Congresses. Portrait by Spencer Baird Nichols.

JOHN BELL, Tennessee: Speaker, second session Twenty-third Congress. Portrait by Willie Betty Newman.

JAMES K. POLK, Tennessee: Speaker, Twenty-fourth and Twenty-fifth Congresses. Portrait by Rebecca Polk.

ROBERT M. T. HUNTER, Virginia: Speaker, Twenty-sixth Congress. Portrait by Richard N. Brooke.

JOHN WHITE, Kentucky: Speaker, Twenty-seventh Congress. Portrait by Gerard Barry.

JOHN W. JONES, Virginia: Speaker, Twenty-eighth Congress. Portrait by James B. Sword.

JOHN W. DAVIS, Indiana: Speaker, Twenty-ninth Congress. Portrait by W. D. Murphy.

ROBERT C. WINTHROP, Massachusetts: Speaker, Thirtieth Congress. Portrait by Daniel Huntington.

HOWELL G. COBB, Georgia: Speaker, Thirty-first Congress. Portrait by Lucy Stanton.

LINN BOYD, Kentucky: Speaker, Thirty-second and Thirty-third Congresses. Portrait by Stanley Middleton.

NATHANIEL P. BANKS, Massachusetts: Speaker, Thirty-fourth Congress. The portrait painter, Robert Vonnoh, stated that this portrait was painted from life, but represents Mr. Banks at the period of his service as Speaker.

JAMES L. ORR, South Carolina: Speaker, Thirty-fifth Congress. Portrait by Esther Edmonds.

WILLIAM PENNINGTON, New Jersey: Speaker, Thirty-sixth Congress. Portrait by Joseph Lauber.

GALUSHA A. GROW, Pennsylvania: Speaker, Thirty-seventh Congress. Portrait by W. A. Greaves.

SCHUYLER COLFAX, Indiana: Speaker, Thirty-eighth, Thirty-ninth, and Fortieth Congresses. Portrait by Freeman Thorp.

THEODORE M. POMEROY, New York: Elected Speaker the last day of the Fortieth Congress and served but 1 day. Portrait by George L. Clough.

JAMES G. BLAINE, Maine: Speaker, Forty-first, Forty-second, and Forty-third Congresses. Portrait by Freeman Thorp.

MICHAEL KERR, Indiana: Speaker, first session, Forty-fourth Congress. Portrait by Charles A. Gray.

SAMUEL J. RANDALL, Pennsylvania: Speaker, second session, Forty-fourth, Forty-fifth, and Forty-sixth Congresses. Portrait by W. A. Greaves.

J. WARREN KEIFER, Ohio: Speaker, Forty-seventh Congress. Portrait by Charles A. Gray.

JOHN G. CARLISLE, Kentucky: Speaker, Forty-eighth, Forty-ninth, and Fiftieth Congresses. Portrait by Ellen Day Hale.

THOMAS B. REED, Maine: Speaker, Fifty-first, Fifty-fourth, and Fifty-fifth Congresses. Portrait by John Singer Sargent.

CHARLES F. CRISP, Georgia: Speaker, Fifty-second and Fifty-third Congresses. Portrait by Robert Hinckley.

DAVID B. HENDERSON, Iowa: Speaker, Fifty-sixth and Fifty-seventh Congresses. Portrait by Freeman Thorp.

JOSEPH G. CANNON, Illinois: Speaker, Fifty-eighth, Fifty-ninth, Sixtieth, and Sixty-first Congresses. Portrait by W. T. Smedley.

CHAMP CLARK, Missouri: Speaker, Sixty-second, Sixty-third, Sixty-fourth, and Sixty-fifth Congresses. Portrait by Boris Gordon.

FREDERICK H. GILLETTE, Massachusetts: Speaker, Sixty-sixth, Sixty-seventh, and Sixty-eighth Congresses. Portrait by Edmund C. Tarbell.

NICHOLAS LONGWORTH, Ohio: Speaker, Sixty-ninth, Seventieth, and Seventy-first Congresses. Portrait by Robert Doblhoff.

JOHN NANCE GARNER, Texas: Speaker, Seventy-second Congress. Portrait by Seymour Stone.

HENRY T. RAINEY, Illinois: Speaker, Seventy-third Congress. Portrait by Howard Chandler Christy.

JOSEPH W. BYRNS, Tennessee: Speaker, Seventy-fourth Congress. Portrait by Ella Sophonisba Hergesheimer.

WILLIAM B. BANKHEAD, Alabama: Speaker, Seventy-fourth, Seventy-fifth, and Seventy-sixth Congresses. Portrait by Howard Chandler Christy.

SAM RAYBURN, Texas: Speaker, Seventy-sixth, Seventy-seventh, Seventy-eighth, Seventy-ninth, Eighty-first, Eighty-second, Eighty-fourth, Eighty-fifth, Eighty-sixth, and Eighty-seventh Congresses. Portrait by Douglas Chandor.

JOSEPH W. MARTIN, Jr., Massachusetts: Speaker, Eightieth and Eighty-third Congresses. Portrait by Boris Gordon. Temporarily located in Mr. Martin's office, Room H-326.

WILLIAM B. BANKHEAD, Speaker of the House of Representatives, Seventy-fourth, Seventy-fifth, and
Seventy-sixth Congresses
Portrait by Howard Chandler Christy.
Location: Speaker's Lobby, House wing.

19

NATHANIEL P. BANKS, Speaker of the House of Representatives, Thirty-fourth Congress
Portrait by Robert Vonnoh.
Location: Speaker's Lobby, House wing.

PHILIP PENDLETON BARBOUR, Speaker of the House of Representatives, Seventeenth Congress
Portrait by Kake Flournoy Edwards.
Location: Speaker's Lobby, House wing.

JOHN BELL, Speaker of the House of Representatives, second session Twenty-third Congress
Portrait by Willie Betty Newman.
Location: Speaker's Lobby, House wing.

JAMES G. BLAINE, Speaker of the House of Representatives, Forty-first, Forty-second, and Forty-third Congresses
Portrait by Freeman Thorp.
Location: Speaker's Lobby, House wing.

LINN BOYD, Speaker of the House of Representatives, Thirty-second and Thirty-third Congresses
Portrait by Stanley Middleton.
Location: Speaker's Lobby, House wing.

JOSEPH W. BYRNS, Speaker of the House of Representatives, Seventy-fourth Congress
Portrait by Ella Sophonisba Hergesheimer.
Location: Speaker's Lobby, House wing.

JOSEPH G. CANNON, Speaker of the House of Representatives, Fifty-eighth, Fifty-ninth,
Sixtieth and Sixty-first Congresses
Portrait by William T. Smedley.
Location: Speaker's Lobby, House wing.

JOHN G. CARLISLE, Speaker of the House of Representatives, Forty-eighth, Forty-ninth, and Fiftieth Congresses
Portrait by Ellen Day Hale.
Location: Speaker's Lobby, House wing.

LANGDON CHEVES, Speaker of the House of Representatives; second session Thirteenth Congress
Portrait by Hal Morrison.
Location: Speaker's Lobby, House wing.

Boris B. Gordon-1919.

CHAMP CLARK, Speaker of the House of Representatives, Sixty-second, Sixty-third, Sixty-fourth, and Sixty-fifth Congresses
Portrait by Boris Gordon.
Location: Speaker's Lobby, House wing.

HENRY CLAY, Speaker of the House of Representatives, Twelfth and Thirteenth, second session
Fourteenth, Fifteenth, first session Sixteenth, and Eighteenth Congresses
Portrait by Giuseppe Fagnani.
Location: Speaker's Lobby, House wing.

HOWELL G. COBB, Speaker of the House of Representatives, Thirty-first Congress
Portrait by Lucy Stanton.
Location: Speaker's Lobby, House wing.

SCHUYLER COLFAX, Speaker of the House of Representatives, Thirty-eighth, Thirty-ninth, and Fortieth Congresses
Portrait by Freeman Thorp.
Location: Speaker's Lobby, House wing.

CHARLES F. CRISP, Speaker of the House of Representatives, Fifty-second, and Fifty-third Congresses
Portrait by Robert Hinckley.
Location: Speaker's Lobby, House wing.

JOHN W. DAVIS, Speaker of the House of Representatives, Twenty-ninth Congress
Portrait by W. D. Murphy.
Location: Speaker's Lobby, House wing.

JONATHAN DAYTON, Speaker of the House of Representatives, Fourth, and first session of Fifth Congresses
Portrait by Henry Harrison.
Location: Speaker's Lobby, House wing.

JOHN NANCE GARNER, Speaker of the House of Representatives, Seventy-second Congress
Portrait by Seymour Stone.
Location: Speaker's Lobby, House wing.

FREDERICK H. GILLETTE, Speaker of the House of Representatives, Sixty-sixth, Sixty-seventh, and Sixty-eighth Congresses
Portrait by Edmund C. Tarbell.
Location: Speaker's Lobby, House wing.

37

Neg. No. 24992

GALUSHA A. GROW, Speaker of the House of Representatives, Thirty-seventh Congress
Portrait by W. A. Greaves.
Location: Speaker's Lobby, House wing.

38

Neg. No. 24881

DAVID B. HENDERSON, Speaker of the House of Representatives, Fifty-sixth and Fifty-seventh Congresses
Portrait by Freeman Thorp.
Location: Speaker's Lobby, House wing.

ROBERT M. T. HUNTER, Speaker of the House of Representatives, Twenty-sixth Congress
Portrait by Richard N. Brooke.
Location: Speaker's Lobby, House wing.

Neg. No. 24975

JOHN W. JONES, Speaker of the House of Representatives, Twenty-eighth Congress
Portrait by James B. Sword.
Location: Speaker's Lobby, House wing.

39–071 O—65——5

J. WARREN KEIFER, Speaker of the House of Representatives, Forty-seventh Congress
Portrait by Charles A. Gray.
Location: Speaker's Lobby, House wing.

MICHAEL KERR, Speaker of the House of Representatives, first session, Forty-fourth Congress
Portrait by Charles A. Gray.
Location: Speaker's Lobby, House wing.

NICHOLAS LONGWORTH, Speaker of the House of Representatives, Sixty-ninth, Seventieth
and Seventy-first Congresses
Portrait by Robert Doblhoff.
Location: Speaker's Lobby, House wing.

NATHANIEL MACON, Speaker of the House of Representatives, Seventh, Eighth, and Ninth Congresses
Portrait by Robert D. Gauley.
Location: Speaker's Lobby, House wing.

FREDERICK A. C. MUHLENBERG, Speaker of the House of Representatives, First and Third Congresses
Portrait by Samuel B. Waugh, from an early portrait by Joseph Wright.
Location: Speaker's Lobby, House wing.

JAMES L. ORR, Speaker of the House of Representatives, Thirty-fifth Congress
Portrait by Esther Edmonds.
Location: Speaker's Lobby, House wing.

WILLIAM PENNINGTON, Speaker of the House of Representatives, Thirty-sixth Congress
Portrait by Joseph Lauber.
Location: Speaker's Lobby, House wing.

48

JAMES K. POLK, Speaker of the House of Representatives, Twenty-fourth and Twenty-fifth Congresses
Portrait by Rebecca Polk.
Location: Speaker's Lobby, House wing.

THEODORE M. POMEROY, Elected Speaker the last day of the Fortieth Congress and served but 1 day
Portrait by George L. Clough.
Location: Speaker's Lobby, House wing.

HENRY T. RAINEY, Speaker of the House of Representatives, Seventy-third Congress
Portrait by Howard Chandler Christy.
Location: Speaker's Lobby, House wing.

SAMUEL J. RANDALL, Speaker of the House of Representatives, second session, Forty-fourth, Forty-fifth, and Forty-sixth Congresses
Portrait by W. A. Greaves.
Location: Speaker's Lobby, House wing.

SAM RAYBURN, Speaker of the House of Representatives, Seventy-sixth, Seventy-seventh, Seventy-eighth, Seventy-ninth, Eighty-first, Eighty-second, Eighty-fourth, Eighty-fifth, Eighty-sixth, and Eighty-seventh Congresses
Portrait by Douglas Chandor.
Location: Speaker's Lobby, House wing.

53

THOMAS B. REED, Speaker of the House of Representatives, Fifty-first, Fifty-fourth, and Fifty-fifth Congresses
Portrait by John Singer Sargent.
Location: Speaker's Lobby, House wing.

THEODORE SEDGWICK, Speaker of the House of Representatives, Sixth Congress
Portrait by Edgar Parker (copy of original by Gilbert Stuart).
Location: Speaker's Lobby, House wing.

ANDREW STEVENSON, Speaker of the House of Representatives, Twentieth, Twenty-first, Twenty-second, and first session Twenty-third Congresses
Portrait by Spencer Baird Nichols.
Location: Speaker's Lobby, House wing.

JOHN W. TAYLOR, Speaker of the House of Representatives, second session Sixteenth Congress, and Nineteenth
Congress
Portrait by Miss C. L. Ransom.
Location: Speaker's Lobby, House wing.

57

JONATHAN TRUMBULL, Speaker of the House of Representatives, Second Congress
Portrait by H. I. Thompson.
Location: Speaker's Lobby, House wing.

JOSEPH B. VARNUM, Speaker of the House of Representatives, Tenth and Eleventh Congresses
Portrait by Charles L. Elliott.
Location: Speaker's Lobby, House wing.

JOHN WHITE, Speaker of the House of Representatives, Twenty-seventh Congress
Portrait by Gerard Barry.
Location: Speaker's Lobby, House wing.

ROBERT C. WINTHROP, Speaker of the House of Representatives, Thirtieth Congress
Portrait by Daniel Huntington.
Location: Speaker's Lobby, House wing.

SPEAKERS OF THE HOUSE OF REPRESENTATIVES—Continued

Seven Portraits

(Six Crayon Portraits)

(NO ILLUSTRATIONS)

John Bell, crayon portrait by unlisted artist; located in Room H–210, Office of the Speaker of the House of Representatives.

Linn Boyd, crayon portrait by unlisted artist; located in Room H–210, Office of the Speaker of the House of Representatives.

Jonathan Dayton, crayon portrait by unlisted artist; located in Room H–210, Office of the Speaker of the House of Representatives.

James K. Polk, crayon portrait by unlisted artist; located in Room H–210, Office of the Speaker of the House of Representatives.

Andrew Stevenson, crayon portrait by unlisted artist; located in Room H–210, Office of the Speaker of the House of Representatives.

Robert C. Winthrop, crayon portrait by unlisted artist; located in Room H–210, Office of the Speaker of the House of Representatives.

(One Small Oil Portrait)

John W. Taylor, small oil portrait by unlisted artist from an original by Gibson; located in Room H–210, Office of the Speaker of the House of Representatives.

UNITED STATES SENATORS

Twenty-Two Portraits

William B. Allison, portrait by Willbur Aaron Reaser, acquired by purchase in 1909, located in Senate wing, second floor, main corridor.

Charles Carroll of Carrollton, portrait by Chester Harding, acquired by purchase in 1870, located in House wing, third floor, east.

Henry Clay, portrait by Henry F. Darby, acquired by purchase in 1881, located in Senate wing, second floor, main corridor.

Henry Clay, portrait by John Neagle, acquired by purchase in 1871, located in House wing, third floor, east

John Adams Dix, portrait by Imogene Robinson Morrell, acquired by purchase in 1883, located in the Architect's Storeroom.

Arthur P. Gorman, portrait by Louis P. Dieterich, accepted by the Joint Committee on the Library as a gift from his family in 1943. This portrait is located in the Architect's Storeroom.

John Langdon, First President pro tempore of the Senate, portrait by Hattie E. Burdette, acquired by purchase in 1916. Stored in subway storeroom.

Henry Latimer, portrait by Clawson Shakespeare Hammitt, accepted by the Joint Committee on the Library as a gift from Miss Mary R. Latimer in 1916, located in Senate wing, third floor, south corridor.

James Hamilton Lewis, portrait by Louis Betts, accepted by the Joint Committee on the Library as a gift from Mrs. J. Hamilton Lewis in 1940. This portrait is located in the Office of the Senate Majority Leader, Room S–210.

Charles L. McNary, portrait by Henrique Medina, accepted by the Joint Committee on the Library as a gift from friends of the late Senator in 1944, located in the Office of the Senate Bill Clerk, Room S–220.

Justin S. Morrill, portrait by Eastman Johnson, accepted by the Joint Committee on the Library as a gift from Miss Louise S. Swan in 1920, located in Senate wing, second floor, main corridor.

Joseph T. Robinson, portrait by N. R. Brewer, accepted by Senate Resolution 173, Seventy-fifth Congress, August 12, 1937, as a gift from friends of the late Senator, located in the Office of the Senate Majority Leader, Room S–210.

MORRIS SHEPPARD, portrait by Boris B. Gordon, accepted by Senate Resolution 197, Seventy-seventh Congress, November 21, 1941, as a gift from his family. This portrait is located in room S–212, Office of the Vice President.

CHARLES SUMNER, portrait by Walter Ingalls, acquired by purchase in 1886, located in Senate wing, second floor, main corridor.

ALLEN G. THURMAN, portrait by John H. Witt, acquired in early 1900's (records incomplete),

located in the Architect's Storeroom. (No illustration.)

DANIEL WEBSTER, portrait by John Neagle, acquired by purchase in 1881, located in Senate wing, second floor, main corridor.

DANIEL WEBSTER, portrait by James Henry Wright, accepted by Senate Resolution 330, Seventy-eighth Congress, September 21, 1944, as a gift from Mr. Lester Martin, located over the northwest stairway, Senate wing, opposite the President's room. (No illustration.)

(Portraits of Senators—Senate Reception Room, Senate Wing, United States Capitol)

Five portraits of Senators were acquired under Senate Resolution #145 (August 2, 1955), 84th Congress, 1st Session, #297 (July 12, 1956), 84th Congress, 2nd Session, and #174 (August 26, 1957), 85th Congress, 1st Session. Unveiled March 12, 1959.

JOHN C. CALHOUN of South Carolina, by Arthur Conrad

HENRY CLAY of Kentucky, by Allyn Cox

ROBERT M. LA FOLLETTE, SR., of Wisconsin, by Chester La Follette

ROBERT A. TAFT, of Ohio, by Deane Keller

DANIEL WEBSTER of Massachusetts, by Adrian Lamb

Neg. No. 24358
WILLIAM B. ALLISON
Portrait by Willbur Aaron Reaser.
Location: Senate wing, main corridor, second floor.

CHARLES CARROLL of CARROLLTON
Portrait by Chester Harding.
Location: House wing, third floor, east.

HENRY CLAY
Portrait by Henry F. Darby.
Location: Senate wing, main corridor, second floor.

HENRY CLAY
Portrait by John Neagle.
Location: House wing, third floor, east.

JOHN ADAMS DIX
Portrait by Imogene Robinson Morrell.
Location: Architect's Storeroom.

ARTHUR PUE GORMAN
Portrait by Louis P. Dieterich.
Location: Architect's Storeroom.

JOHN LANGDON
Portrait by Hattie E. Burdette.
Location: Stored in subway storeroom.

HENRY LATIMER
Portrait by Clawson Shakespeare Hammitt.
Location: Senate wing, third floor, south corridor.

JAMES HAMILTON LEWIS
Portrait by Louis Betts.
Location: Senate wing, second floor, Room S-210.

71

Neg. No. 24318

CHARLES L McNARY
Portrait by Henrique Medina.
Location: Office of the Senate Bill Clerk, Room S–220.

JUSTIN S. MORRILL
Portrait by Eastman Johnson.
Location: Senate wing, main corridor, second floor.

39–071 O—65——7

JOSEPH T. ROBINSON
Portrait by N. R. Brewer.
Location: Senate wing, second floor, Room S–210.

Neg. No. 25980

MORRIS SHEPPARD
Portrait by Boris B. Gordon.
Location: Senate wing, second floor, Room S–212.   Office of the Vice President.

75

CHARLES SUMNER
Portrait by Walter Ingalls.
Location: Senate wing, main corridor, second floor.

DANIEL WEBSTER
Portrait by John Neagle.
Location: Senate wing, main corridor, second floor.

JOHN C. CALHOUN
Portrait by Arthur Conrad.
Location: Senate Reception Room, Senate wing.

Neg. No. 14294

HENRY CLAY
Portrait by Allyn Cox.
Location: Senate Reception Room, Senate wing.

ROBERT M. La FOLLETTE, SR.
Portrait by Chester La Follette.
Location: Senate Reception Room, Senate wing.

ROBERT A. TAFT
Portrait by Deane Keller.
Location: Senate Reception Room, Senate wing.

81

DANIEL WEBSTER
Portrait by Adrian Lamb.
Location: Senate Reception Room, Senate wing.

CHAIRMEN OF THE HOUSE COMMITTEE ON APPROPRIATIONS

Twenty-One Portraits (Oil and Crayon), Photographs, and Engravings

This collection includes all chairmen of the House Committee on Appropriations from Thaddeus Stevens, Thirty-ninth Congress, through Edward T. Taylor, Seventy-seventh Congress. The collection was of gradual growth and represented gifts to the committee by members or friends. It being the view of members of the House Appropriations Committee and the Joint Committee on the Library that these portraits, photographs, and engravings belonged to the committee, as distinguished from the House, the Senate, or the Congress, they were formally offered by the chairman of the House Appropriations Committee, Mr. Taylor, to the Joint Committee on the Library in 1940, and were accepted by the Joint Committee on the Library, by committee resolution, November 18, 1940, on behalf of Congress, as an addition to the art collection of the Capitol. The photograph of Thaddeus Stevens was not included as it was not acquired until a later date.

NAME OF CHAIRMAN	STATE	PERIOD OF SERVICE AS CHAIRMAN	DESCRIPTION	NAME OF ARTIST
Thaddeus Stevens	Pennsylvania	1865–68	Photograph enlarged and tinted with oil, Mathew Brady.	
Elihu B. Washburne*	Illinois	1868–69	Photograph	
Henry L. Dawes*	Massachusetts	1869–71	.. do	
James A. Garfield	Ohio	1871–75	Oil portrait	C. Adele Fassett.
Samuel J. Randall	Pennsylvania	1875–76 / 1883–89	Crayon portrait	C. Adele Fassett.
William S. Holman*	Indiana	1876–77 / 1891–93	Photograph	
John D. C. Atkins*	Tennessee	1877–81	.. do	
Frank Hiscock*	New York	1881–83	.. do	
Joseph G. Cannon	Illinois	1889–91 / 1895–1903	Oil portrait	Freeman Thorp.
Joseph D. Sayers*	Texas	1893–95	Photograph	
James A. Hemenway*	Indiana	1903–05	.. do	
James A. Tawney	Minnesota	1905–11	Oil portrait	Freeman Thorp.
John J. Fitzgerald	New York	1911–17	.. do	Kenyon Cox.
J. Swagar Sherley	Kentucky	1918–19	.. do	Charles S. Williams.
James W. Good	Iowa	1919–21	.. do	John C. Johansen.
Martin B. Madden	Illinois	1921–28	Photograph enlarged and tinted with oil.	
Daniel R. Anthony	Kansas	1928–29	Photograph	
William R. Wood	Indiana	1929–31	Oil portrait	George B. Matthews.
Joseph W. Byrns	Tennessee	1931–33	.. do	George B. Matthews.
James P. Buchanan	Texas	1933–37	.. do	Seymour Stone.
Edward T. Taylor	Colorado	1937–41	.. do	John C. Johansen.

*No Illustration.

Neg. No. 22875

DANIEL R. ANTHONY, Chairman of the House Committee on Appropriations, 1928–29
Photograph.
Location: House Appropriations Committee Room.

84

JAMES P. BUCHANAN, Chairman of the House Committee on Appropriations, 1933–37
Portrait by Seymour Stone.
Location: House Appropriations Committee Room.

JOSEPH W. BYRNS, Chairman of the House Committee on Appropriations, 1931–33
Portrait by George B. Matthews.
Location: House Appropriations Committee Room.

Neg. No. 24098

JOSEPH G. CANNON, Chairman of the House Committee on Appropriations, 1889–91; 1895–1903
Portrait by Freeman Thorp.
Location: House Appropriations Committee Room.

JOHN J. FITZGERALD, Chairman of the House Committee on Appropriations, 1911–17
Portrait by Kenyon Cox.
Location: House Appropriations Committee Room.

JAMES A. GARFIELD, Chairman of the House Committee on Appropriations, 1871–75
Portrait by C. Adele Fassett.
Location: House Appropriations Committee Room.

JAMES W. GOOD, Chairman of the House Committee on Appropriations, 1919–21
Portrait by John C. Johansen.
Location: House Appropriations Committee Room.

MARTIN B. MADDEN, Chairman of the House Committee on Appropriations, 1921–28
Photograph enlarged and tinted with oil.
Location: House Appropriations Committee Room.

SAMUEL J. RANDALL, Chairman of the House Committee on Appropriations, 1875–76, 1883–89
Crayon portrait by C. Adele Fassett.
Location: House Appropriations Committee Room.

J. SWAGER SHERLEY, Chairman of the House Committee on Appropriations, 1918–19
Portrait by Charles S. Williams.
Location: House Appropriations Committee Room.

93

THADDEUS STEVENS, Chairman of the House Committee on Appropriations, 1865–68
Enlarged tinted photograph by Mathew Brady.
Location: House Appropriations Committee Room.

JAMES A. TAWNEY, Chairman of the House Committee on Appropriations, 1905–11
Portrait by Freeman Thorp.
Location: House Appropriations Committee Room.

EDWARD T. TAYLOR, Chairman of the House Committee on Appropriations, 1937–41
Portrait by John C. Johansen.
Location: House Appropriations Committee Room.

Neg. No. 22876

WILLIAM R. WOOD, Chairman of the House Committee on Appropriations, 1929–31
Portrait by George B. Matthews.
Location: House Appropriations Committee Room.

97

ARCHITECTS OF THE CAPITOL

Seven Portraits

WILLIAM THORNTON, Architect of the Capitol from 1793 to 1794, portrait by George B. Matthews; acquired in 1931 through employment of the artist at the Capitol; located in the Office of the Architect of the Capitol, Room SB–14.

BENJAMIN H. LATROBE, Architect of the Capitol from 1803 to 1811 and 1815 to 1817, portrait by George B. Matthews; acquired in 1931 through employment of the artist at the Capitol; located in the Office of the Architect of the Capitol, Room SB–14.

CHARLES BULFINCH, Architect of the Capitol from 1818 to 1829, portrait by George B. Matthews; acquired in 1931 through employment of the artist at the Capitol; located in the Office of the Architect of the Capitol, Room SB–14.

THOMAS U. WALTER, Architect of the Capitol from 1851 to 1865, portrait by Francisco Pausas; accepted as a gift from Clark Walter, grandson of Architect Walter, for the Office of the Architect of the Capitol in 1926; located in the Office of the Architect of the Capitol, Room SB–14.

EDWARD CLARK, Architect of the Capitol from 1865 to 1902, portrait by Constantino Brumidi; accepted by the Joint Committee on the Library as a gift from the Clark family for the Office of the Architect of the Capitol in 1929; located in the Office of the Architect of the Capitol, Room SB–14.

ELLIOTT WOODS, Architect of the Capitol from 1902 to 1923, portrait by George B. Matthews; acquired in 1931 through employment of the artist at the Capitol; located in the Office of the Architect of the Capitol, Room SB–14.

DAVID LYNN, Architect of the Capitol from 1923 to 1954, portrait by Charles J. Fox; acquired by purchase in 1956; (Public Law 624, 84th Congress, 2nd Session.) Located in the Office of the Architect of the Capitol, Room SB–14.

Neg. No. 716

CHARLES BULFINCH
Portrait by George B. Matthews.
Location: Office of the Architect of the Capitol.

EDWARD CLARK
Portrait by Constantino Brumidi.
Location: Office of the Architect of the Capitol.

BENJAMIN H. LATROBE
Portrait by George B. Matthews.
Location: Office of the Architect of the Capitol.

100

DAVID LYNN
Portrait by Charles J. Fox.
Location: Office of the Architect of the Capitol.

WILLIAM THORNTON
Portrait by George B. Matthews.
Location: Office of the Architect of the Capitol.

THOMAS U. WALTER
Portrait by Francisco Pausas.
Location: Office of the Architect of the Capitol.

ELLIOTT WOODS
Portrait by George B. Matthews.
Location: Office of the Architect of the Capitol.

PROMINENT INDIVIDUALS

Eleven Portraits

Members of the Continental Congress

GUNNING BEDFORD, JR., portrait by Charles Willson Peale; acquired as a bequest under the will of Henrietta Bedford in 1872; located in the House wing, third floor, east corridor. Delegate to the Continental Congress from Delaware 1783–85; member of the Federal constitutional convention at Philadelphia in 1787 and signer of the Constitution.

HENRY LAURENS, portrait by John Singleton Copley; acquired by purchase in 1886; located in the Office of the Senate Majority Leader, Room S–209. Delegate to the Continental Congress from South Carolina, elected in January 1777 and served as its President from November 1777 to December 9, 1778; Minister to Holland. While en route to his post, he was captured and held prisoner in the Tower of London for fifteen months and was exchanged for Lord Cornwallis.

PATRICK HENRY, portrait by George B. Matthews; acquired about 1900 (records incomplete) through employment of the artist at the Capitol; located in the Senate wing, second floor, main corridor. Delegate to the Continental Congress from Virginia 1774–1776; American statesman and orator; Governor of Virginia.

Members of Congress

JOSHUA R. GIDDINGS, portrait by Caroline L. Ormes Ransom; acquired by purchase in 1867; located in the Architect's Storeroom. A Representative from Ohio; served in the Congresses intermittently from 1838 to 1859.

Chief Justices

JOHN MARSHALL, portrait by Richard N. Brooke, from the original painted in 1858–59 by W. D. Washington; acquired by purchase in 1881; located in the House wing, third floor, west corridor. Chief Justice of the United States, 1801–1835; soldier in the Revolutionary War; Member of Congress from Virginia and Secretary of State.

Military and Naval Leaders

JOHN PAUL JONES, portrait by George B. Matthews; acquired by purchase about 1890–1900 (records incomplete); located in the Senate Armed Services Committee Room, 212 Senate Office Building; American naval officer in the Revolutionary War.

GENERAL LAFAYETTE, portrait by Ary Scheffer; accepted by the House of Representatives as a gift from the artist in 1824; located on the south wall of the House Chamber. French statesman and General; served as volunteer in the Continental Army in the American Revolution.

JAMES LATIMER, portrait by Clawson Shakespeare Hammitt; accepted by the Joint Committee on the Library as a gift from Mary R. Latimer in 1916; located in the Senate wing, third floor, south corridor. Lieutenant Colonel in the Continental Army; presided over the Delaware Convention for the ratification of the Constitution, (Delaware was the first State to ratify); lawyer.

GENERAL GEORGE THOMAS, portrait by Caroline L. Ormes Ransom; acquired as a bequest under the will of the artist in 1910; located in the Architect's Storeroom. Served in the Mexican War; gained the nickname "The Rock of Chickamauga" for gallantry during the Battle of Chickamauga during the Civil War. (No illustration.)

39–071 O—65——9

CARLO FRANZONI, portrait by Pietro Bonanni; accepted by the Joint Committee on the Library as a gift from Dr. Charles H. Franzoni, in 1924 for the Office of the Architect of the Capitol; located in the Office of the Architect of the Capitol, Room SB–15. Sculptor of the Car of History, also known as the Franzoni clock, in Statuary Hall.

POCAHONTAS, portrait by unlisted artist; accepted by Senate Resolution of February 28, 1899, as a gift from Henry S. Wellcome; located in the Senate Disbursing Office, Room S–233. American Indian princess; reputed to have saved Captain John Smith from execution.

GUNNING BEDFORD, JR.
Portrait by Charles Willson Peale.
Location: House wing, third floor, east corridor.

Neg. No. 25063

CARLO FRANZONI
Portrait by Pietro Bonnani.
Location: Office of the Architect of the Capitol.

JOSHUA R. GIDDINGS
Portrait by Caroline L. Ormes Ransom.
Location: Architect's Storeroom.

PATRICK HENRY
Portrait by George B. Matthews.
Location: Senate wing, second floor, main corridor.

JOHN PAUL JONES
Portrait by George B. Matthews.
Location: Senate Armed Services Committee Room, Senate Office Building.

GENERAL LAFAYETTE
Portrait by Ary Scheffer.
Location: south wall of the House Chamber.

JAMES LATIMER
Portrait by Clawson Shakespeare Hammitt.
Location: Senate wing, third floor, south corridor.

112

Neg. No. 314

HENRY LAURENS
Portrait by John Singleton Copley.
Location: Office of the Senate Majority Leader

JOHN MARSHALL
Portrait by Richard N. Brooke.
Location: House wing, third floor, west corridor.

Ætatis suæ 21. Aº 1616.

Matoaks als Rebecka daughter to the mighty Prince
Powhatan Emperour of Attanoughkomouck als Virginia
converted and baptized in the Christian faith, and
Wife to the Worth Mr Tho: Rolff.

Neg. No. 24315

POCAHONTAS
Portrait by an unlisted artist.
Location: Senate Disbursing Office.

Paintings Located in the United States Capitol

EIGHT HISTORIC PAINTINGS LOCATED IN THE ROTUNDA

DECLARATION OF INDEPENDENCE IN CONGRESS, AT THE INDEPENDENCE HALL, PHILADELPHIA, JULY 4TH, 1776, by John Trumbull; acquired by purchase, $8,000, 1817–1824.

SURRENDER OF GENERAL BURGOYNE AT SARATOGA, NEW YORK, OCTOBER 17TH, 1777, by John Trumbull; acquired by purchase, $8,000, 1817–1824.

SURRENDER OF LORD CORNWALLIS AT YORKTOWN, VIRGINIA, OCTOBER 19TH, 1781, by John Trumbull; acquired by purchase, $8,000, 1817–1824.

GENERAL GEORGE WASHINGTON RESIGNING HIS COMMISSION TO CONGRESS AS COMMANDER IN CHIEF OF THE ARMY AT ANNAPOLIS, MARYLAND, DECEMBER 23D, 1783, by John Trumbull; acquired by purchase, $8,000, 1817–1824.

EMBARKATION OF THE PILGRIMS AT DELFT HAVEN, HOLLAND, JULY 22ND, 1620, by Robert W. Weir; acquired by purchase, $10,000, 1837–1847.

LANDING OF COLUMBUS AT THE ISLAND OF GUANAHANI, WEST INDIES, OCTOBER 12TH, 1492, by John Vanderlyn; acquired by purchase, $10,000, 1837–1847.

DISCOVERY OF THE MISSISSIPPI BY DE SOTO A.D. 1541, by William H. Powell; acquired by purchase, $12,000, 1847–1855.

BAPTISM OF POCAHONTAS AT JAMESTOWN, VIRGINIA, 1613, by John G. Chapman; acquired by purchase, $10,000, 1837–1847.

BAPTISM OF POCAHONTAS At Jamestown, Virginia, 1613
Painting by John G. Chapman.
Location: Rotunda.

1. Pocahontas
2. John Rolfe
3. Alexander Whiteaker
4. Sir Thomas Dale
5. Sister of Pocahontas
6. Nantequaus, brother of Pocahontas
7. Opechancanough
8. Opachisco, uncle of Pocahontas

9. Richard Wyffin
10. Standard bearer
11. Mr. and Mrs. Forrest, the lady being the first gentlewoman to arrive in the colony
12. Henry Spilman
13. John and Anne Laydon, the first persons married in the colony
14. The page

117

DECLARATION OF INDEPENDENCE In Congress, at the Independence Hall, Philadelphia, July 4th, 1776
Painting by John Trumbull.
Location: Rotunda.

DECLARATION OF INDEPENDENCE

In Congress, at the Independence Hall, Philadelphia, July 4ᵗʰ 1776.

1. George Wythe, Virginia
2. William Whipple, New Hampshire
3. Josiah Bartlett, New Hampshire
4. Benjamin Harrison, Virginia
5. Thomas Lynch, South Carolina
6. Richard Henry Lee, Virginia
7. Samuel Adams, Massachusetts
8. George Clinton, New York
9. William Paca, Maryland
10. Samuel Chase, Maryland
11. Lewis Morris, New York
12. William Floyd, New York
13. Arthur Middleton, South Carolina
14. Thomas Heyward, jr., South Carolina
15. Charles Carroll, Maryland
16. George Walton, Georgia

17. Robert Morris, Pennsylvania
18. Thomas Willing, Pennsylvania
19. Benjamin Rush, Pennsylvania
20. Elbridge Gerry, Massachusetts
21. Robert Treat Paine, Massachusetts
22. Abraham Clark, New Jersey
23. Stephen Hopkins, Rhode Island
24. William Ellery, Rhode Island
25. George Clymer, Pennsylvania
26. William Hooper, North Carolina
27. Joseph Hewes, North Carolina
28. James Willson, Pennsylvania
29. Francis Hopkinson, New Jersey
30. John Adams, Massachusetts
31. Roger Sherman, Connecticut
32. Robert R. Livingston, New York

33. Thomas Jefferson, Virginia
34. Benjamin Franklin, Pennsylvania
35. Richard Stockton, New Jersey
36. Francis Lewis, New York
37. John Witherspoon, New Jersey
38. Samuel Huntington, Connecticut
39. William Williams, Connecticut
40. Oliver Wolcott, Connecticut
41. John Hancock, Massachusetts
42. Charles Thomson (Secretary), Pennsylvania
43. George Read, Delaware
44. John Dickinson, Pennsylvania
45. Edward Rutledge, South Carolina
46. Thomas McKean, Delaware
47. Philip Livingston, New York

There were 56 signers of the Declaration of Independence. The Key to the painting, "Declaration of Independence," shows a total of 47 persons. Five of the 47 portrayed *were not* signers of the Declaration of Independence.

GEORGE CLINTON, (New York)
ROBERT R. LIVINGSTON, (New York)
THOMAS WILLING, (Pennsylvania)

CHARLES THOMSON, (Pennsylvania)
JOHN DICKINSON, (Pennsylvania)

There were fourteen signers whose portraits do not appear in the painting in the Rotunda of the Capitol, viz:

MATTHEW THORNTON, (New Hampshire)
JOHN HART, (New Jersey)
JOHN MORTON, (Pennsylvania)
JAMES SMITH, (Pennsylvania)
GEORGE TAYLOR, (Pennsylvania)
GEORGE ROSS, (Pennsylvania)
CAESAR RODNEY, (Delaware)

THOMAS STONE, (Maryland)
THOMAS NELSON, Jr., (Virginia)
FRANCIS LIGHTFOOT LEE, (Virginia)
CARTER BRAXTON, (Virginia)
JOHN PENN, (North Carolina)
BUTTON GWINNETT, (Georgia)
LYMAN HALL, (Georgia)

DISCOVERY OF THE MISSISSIPPI BY DE SOTO A.D. 1541
Painting by William H. Powell.
Location: Rotunda.

DE SOTO'S DISCOVERY OF THE MISSISSIPPI
A.D 1541

1. De Soto
2. Moorish servant
3. Confessor
4. Young Spanish cavalier
5. Cannon dragged up by artillerymen
6. Company of stalwart men planting a cross
7. Ecclesiastic bearing the censer
8. Old priest blessing the cross

9. Soldier dressing his wounded leg
10. Camp chest with arms, helmets, and other implements of war
11. Group of standard bearers and helmeted men
12. Two young Indian maidens
13. Indian chiefs bearing the pipe of peace

In the distance is seen the Mississippi. Its waters are broken by glancing canoes, magical islands, and purple shores

120

EMBARKATION OF THE PILGRIMS At Delft Haven, Holland, July 22nd, 1620
Painting by Robert W. Weir.
Location: Rotunda.

1. Mr. Robinson, pastor of the congregation
2. Elder William Brewster
3. Mrs. Brewster and sick child
4. Governor Carver
5. William Bradford
6. Mr. and Mrs. White
7. Mr. and Mrs. Winslow
8. Mr. and Mrs. Fuller
9. Miles Standish and his wife Rose
10. Mrs. Bradford; she fell overboard the day the vessel came to anchor
11. Mrs. Carver and child
12. Captain Reynolds and sailor
13. Boy belonging to Carver and family
14. Boy in charge of Mr. Winslow
15. Boy belonging to Mrs. Winslow's family
16. A nurse and child

121

GENERAL GEORGE WASHINGTON RESIGNING HIS COMMISSION to Congress as Commander in Chief
of the Army at Annapolis, Maryland, December 23d, 1783
Painting by John Trumbull.
Location: Rotunda

GEN. WASHINGTON RESIGNING HIS COMMISSION
to Congress at Annapolis Md. Decemb. 23ᵈ 1783

1. Thomas Mifflin, Pennsylvania, President
   Delegate
2. Charles Thompson, Pennsylvania
   Secretary
3. Elbridge Gerry, Massachusetts
   Delegate
4. Hugh Williamson, North Carolina
   Delegate
5. Samuel Osgood, Massachusetts
   Delegate
6. Eleazer McComb, Delaware
   Delegate
7. George Partridge, Massachusetts
   Delegate
8. Edward Lloyd, Maryland
   Delegate
9. Richard D. Spaight, North Carolina
   Delegate
10. Benjamin Hawkins, North Carolina
    Delegate

11. Abiel Foster, New Hampshire
    Delegate
12. Thomas Jefferson, Virginia
    Delegate
13. Arthur Lee, Virginia
    Delegate
14. David Howell, Rhode Island
    Delegate
15. James Monroe, Virginia
    Delegate
16. Jacob Read, South Carolina
    Delegate
17. James Madison, Virginia
    Spectator
18. William Ellery, Rhode Island
    Delegate
19. J. Townley Chase, Maryland
    Delegate
20. Samuel Hardy, Virginia
    Delegate

21. Charles Morris, Pennsylvania
    Delegate
22. General Washington
23. Col. Benjamin Walker
    Aid-de-camp
24. Col. David Humphreys
    Aid-de-camp
25. General Smallwood, Maryland
    Spectator
26. Gen. Otho Holland Williams, Maryland
    Spectator
27. Col. Samuel Smith, Maryland
    Spectator
28. Col. John E. Howard, Maryland
    Spectator
29. Charles Carroll and two daughters, Maryland
30. Mrs. Washington and her three grandchildren
31. Daniel of St. Jennifer, Maryland
    Spectator

122

LANDING OF COLUMBUS At the Island of Guanahani, West-Indies, October 12th, 1492
Painting by John Vanderlyn.
Location: Rotunda.

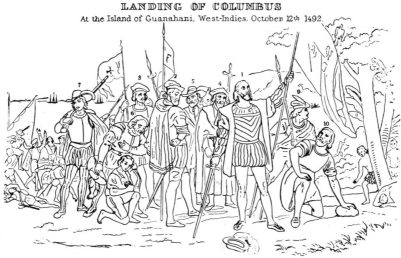

LANDING OF COLUMBUS
At the Island of Guanahani, West-Indies. October 12th 1492.

1. Columbus
2. Martin Alonzo Pinzon
3. Vincent Yannez Pinzon
4. Rodrigo des Escobedo or Escobar, notary of the armament
5. Roderigo Sanchez, inspector of armament
6. Mutineer in a suppliant attitude
7. Alonzo de Ojeda
8. Cabin boy in kneeling posture

9. Soldier whose attention is partly diverted from the ceremony by the appearance of the awe-stricken natives in the forest
10. Sailor in attitude of veneration for the admiral
11. Friar bearing a crucifix

In the distance, groups express joy and hilarity on their landing. Two figures somewhat nearer are contending for glittering particles in the sand. The three vessels—Santa Maria, Pinta, and Nina—are seen in the distance

123

SURRENDER OF GENERAL BURGOYNE At Saratoga, New York, October 17th, 1777
Painting by John Trumbull.
Location: Rotunda.

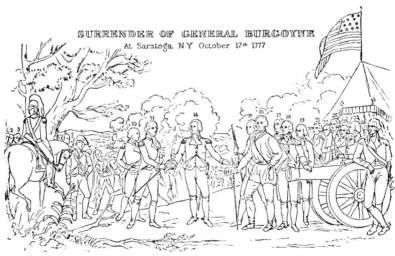

1. Major Lithgow, Massachusetts
2. Colonel Cilly, New Hampshire
3. General Stark, New Hampshire
4. Captain Seymour, of Shelton's Horse
5. Major Hull, Massachusetts
6. Colonel Greaton, Massachusetts
7. Major Dearborne, New Hampshire
8. Colonel Scammell, New Hampshire
9. Colonel Lewis, quartermaster general, New Hampshire
10. Major General Phillips, British

11. Lieutenant General Burgoyne, British
12. General Baron Riedesel, German
13. Colonel Wilkinson, deputy adjutant general, American
14. General Gates
15. Colonel Prescott, Massachusetts Volunteers
16. Colonel Morgan, Virginia Riflemen
17. Brig. Gen. Rufus Putnam, Massachusetts
18. Lieut. Col. John Brooks, late Governor of Massachusetts
19. Rev. Mr. Hitchcock, chaplain, Rhode Island

20. Maj. Rob. Troup, aid-de-camp, New York
21. Major Haskell
22. Major Armstrong
23. Maj. Gen. Philip Schuyler, Albany
24. Brigadier General Glover, Massachusetts
25. Brigadier General Whipple, New Hampshire Militia
26. Maj. M. Clarkson, aid-de-camp, New York
27. Maj. Ebenezer Stevens, Massachusetts, Commanding the artillery

124

SURRENDER OF LORD CORNWALLIS At Yorktown, Virginia, October 19th, 1781
Painting by John Trumbull.
Location: Rotunda.

1. *Count Deuzponts*
   Colonel of French Infantry
2. *Duke de Laval Montmorency*
   Colonel of French Infantry
3. *Count Custine*
   Colonel of French Infantry
4. *Duke de Lauzun*
   Colonel of French Cavalry
5. *General Choizy*
6. *Viscount Viomenil*
7. *Marquis de St. Simon*
8. *Count Fersen*
   Aid-de-camp of Count Rochambeau
9. *Count Charles Damas*
   Aid-de-camp of Count Rochambeau
10. *Marquis Chastellux*
11. *Baron Viomenil*

12. *Count de Barras*
    Admiral
13. *Count de Grasse*
    Admiral
14. *Count Rochambeau*
    General en Chef des Francais
15. *General Lincoln*
16. *E. Stevens*
    Colonel of American Artillery
17. *General Washington*
    Commander in Chief
18. *Thomas Nelson*
    Governor of Virginia
19. *Marquis Lafayette*
20. *Baron Steuben*
21. *Colonel Cobb*
    Aid-de-camp to General Washington
22. *Colonel Trumbull*
    Secretary to General Washington

23. *Maj. Gen. James Clinton, New York*
24. *General Gist, Maryland*
25. *Gen. Anthony Wayne, Pennsylvania*
26. *General Hand, Pennsylvania*
    Adjutant General
27. *Gen. Peter Muhlenberg, Pennsylvania*
28. *Maj. Gen. Henry Knox*
    Commander of Artillery
29. *Lieut. Col. E. Huntington*
    Acting aid-de-camp of General Lincoln
30. *Col. Timothy Pickering*
    Quartermaster General
31. *Col. Alexander Hamilton*
    Commanding Light Infantry
32. *Col. John Laurens, South Carolina*
33. *Col. Walter Stuart, Philadelphia*
34. *Col. Nicholas Fish, New York*

125

TWELVE PAINTINGS LOCATED IN THE SENATE WING OF THE CAPITOL

THE BATTLE OF CHAPULTEPEC (STORMING OF CHAPULTEPEC), by James Walker; acquired by purchase in 1857–1862; in storage.

THE BATTLE OF FORT MOULTRIE, by John Blake White; accepted by the Joint Committee on the Library as a gift from Dr. Octavius A. White in 1901; located in Senate wing, third floor, south corridor.

THE BATTLE OF LAKE ERIE, by William H. Powell; acquired by purchase under contract of 1865; located in Senate wing, east staircase.

THE FIRST READING OF THE EMANCIPATION PROCLAMATION, by Francis Bicknell Carpenter; accepted by Public Resolution 6, Forty-fifth Congress, February 1, 1878, as a gift from Mrs. Elizabeth Thompson; located in Senate wing, west staircase.

THE ELECTORAL COMMISSION OF 1877 (Florida Case) by Cornelia A. Fassett. (The disputed election of 1876 between Hays and Tilden). Acquired by purchase in the late 1880's; located in Senate wing, third floor, east corridor.

GENERAL MARION INVITING A BRITISH OFFICER TO SHARE HIS MEAL, by John Blake White; accepted by the Committee on the Library of the Senate as a gift from Dr. Octavius A. White in 1899; located in Senate wing, third floor, south corridor.

LEIV EIRIKSSON DISCOVERS AMERICA, A.D. 1000, by Per Krohg; accepted by Public Resolution 78, 74th Congress, as a gift from Norwegian friends of America through Dr. Alf Bjercke of Oslo, Norway, in 1936; located in Senate wing, third floor, east corridor. It is a copy of Christian Krohg's famous picture (1893) in the National Gallery at Oslo, Norway, and has been executed by the artist's son, Per Krohg.

MISS MOTT DIRECTING GENERALS MARION AND LEE TO BURN HER MANSION TO DISLODGE THE BRITISH, by John Blake White; accepted by the Committee on the Library of the Senate as a gift from Dr. Octavius A. White in 1899; located in Senate wing, third floor, south corridor.

NIAGARA FALLS IN WINTER, by Regis Gignoux; accepted by the Joint Committee on the Library as a gift from Mrs. Charles Carroll of Doughoregan Manor, Maryland in 1901; located in Senate wing, third floor, south corridor.

THE RECALL OF COLUMBUS, by Augustus G. Heaton; acquired by purchase in 1883; located in Senate wing, third floor, east corridor.

SERGEANTS JASPER AND NEWTON RESCUING AMERICAN PRISONERS FROM THE BRITISH, by John Blake White; accepted by the Committee on the Library of the Senate as a gift from Dr. Octavius A. White in 1899; located in Senate wing, third floor, south corridor.

WE, by Einar Kverne. Picturing Lindbergh's plane as a tiny spot against the sky—Colonel Charles A. Lindbergh's flight—New York to Paris—3,600 miles in 33½ hours, May 20-21, 1927. Presented to the Government by Robert W. Woodruff of Atlanta, Georgia. Accepted by the Joint Committee on the Library May 21, 1928, and hung in the Senate Committee Room of Territories and Insular Possessions (later known as Interior and Insular Affairs)—Room G-23 now Room S-310. Present location not established. (No illustration.)

BATTLE OF CHAPULTEPEC (STORMING OF CHAPULTEPEC)
Painting by James Walker.
Location: in storage.

BATTLE OF FORT MOULTRIE
Painting by John Blake White.
Located in Senate wing, third floor, south corridor.

THE FIRST READING OF THE EMANCIPATION PROCLAMATION
Painting by Francis Bicknell Carpenter.
Location: Senate wing, west staircase.

*KEY TO THE FIRST READING OF THE EMANCIPATION PROCLAMATION**

1. *Abraham Lincoln*
   President
2. *William H. Seward*
   Secretary of State
3. *Salmon P. Chase*
   Secretary of the Treasury
4. *Edwin M. Stanton*
   Secretary of War

5. *Gideon Welles*
   Secretary of the Navy
6. *Edward Bates*
   Attorney General
7. *Montgomery Blair*
   Postmaster General
8. *Caleb B. Smith*
   Secretary of the Interior

*The above key is for the engraving by A. H. Ritchie. The difference between the painting in the Capitol and the engraving is in the postures and accessories.

129

BATTLE OF LAKE ERIE
Painting by William H. Powell.
Location: Senate wing, east staircase.

THE ELECTORAL COMMISSION OF 1877 (The Florida Case)
Painting by Cornelia Adele Fassett.
Location: Senate wing, third floor, east corridor.

Key to Mrs. Fassett's Picture.

The Electoral Commission of 1877 (The Florida Case).

IN THE GALLERY.
(The Press.)

1. W. H. ROBERTS, New Orleans Times.
2. JOHN M. CARSON, New York Times.
3. BEN. PERLEY POORE, Boston Journal.
4. GEORGE W. ADAMS, New York World.
5. T. C. CRAWFORD, Chicago Times.
6. A. M. GIBSON, New York Sun.
7. W. SCOTT SMITH, New York Evening Post.
8. C. W. FITCH, Pittsburgh Chronicle.
9. H. BOYNTON, Cincinnati Gazette.
10. WILSON J. VANCE, Cincinnati Commercial.
11. Mrs. JANE G. SWISSHELM.
12. L. A. GOBRIGHT, N.Y. Associated Press.
13. Mrs. S. J. LIPPINCOTT, ("Grace Greenwood,") N.Y. Tribune.
14. Miss AUSTINE SNEAD, ("Miss Grundy,") N.Y. Graphic.
15. Miss EMMA JANES, Toledo Blade, &c.
16. Mrs. MARY E. NEALY, Home Journal.
17. Mrs. M. D. LINCOLN, ("Bessie Beech,") Cleveland Plain-dealer.
18. Miss SALLIE WOODBURY, ("Ruby Wood,") National Union.
19. Mrs. FANNIE B. WARD, New Orleans Picayune.
20. Mrs. ADELE M. GARRIGUES, Courier, East Saginaw, Mich.
21. W. M. OLIN, Boston Advertiser.
22. W. O. FISHBACK, St. Louis Republican.
23. De-B. R. KEIM, Philadelphia Press.
24. CROSBY S. NOYES, Ed. Evening Star, Washington, D.C.
25. JAMES R. YOUNG, Philadelphia Evening Star.
26. W. CURTIS, Chicago Inter-Ocean.
27. E. B. WIGHT, Chicago Tribune.
28. E. H. LUTHER, Boston Post.
29. CHARLES NORDHOFF, New York Herald.
30. CLIFFORD WARDEN, Pittsburgh Telegraph.
31. F. A. RICHARDSON, Baltimore Sun.
32. E. V. SMALLEY, New York
33. L. Q. WASHINGTON, Louisville Courier-Journal.
34. Mrs. E. S. CROMWELL, Chicago Herald.
35. Mrs. NELLIE S. STOWELL, Kansas City Journal.
36. Mrs. FAYETTA C. SNEAD, ("Fay,") Louisville Courier-Journal.
37. Mrs. A. ROWLAND, Oxford (Pa.) Press.
38. FRANK HATTON, Ed. Burlington Hawkeye.
39. E. STODDARD JOHNSON, Frankfort Yeoman.
40. A. C. BUELL, The Capital.
41. Mrs. A. D. JOHNSTON, Rochester Democrat and Chronicle.
42. Miss MARY E. MANN, Troy Daily Times.
43. CHARLES L. FLANAGAN, Philadelphia North American.
44. Mrs. ELVIRA BLISS SHELDON, ("Aunt True,") Grand Rapids Eagle.
45. W. HARRY CLARKE, National Associated Press.
46. I. N. BURRITT, Ed. Washington Herald.
47. C. CATHCART TAYLOR, Philadelphia Times.
48. WM. P. COPELAND, New York Times.
49. E. F. WATERS, Prop. Boston Commercial Bulletin.
50. J. EDWARDS CLARKE, New York Mail.
51. JNO. C. BURCH, Ed. Nashville American.
52. Mr. GODDARD, Ed. Boston Advertiser.
53. HOWARD CARROL, New York Times.
54. S. H. KAUFFMANN, Evening Star.
55. WM. C. MAC BRIDE, Cincinnati Enquirer.
56. Z. L. WHITE, New York Tribune.
57. EDWIN FLEMING, N.Y. Journal of Commerce.
58. L. W. KENNEDY, Daily Chronicle, Washington, D.C.
59. M. J. DEE, Detroit Evening News.
60. GEORGE DOUGLAS, Washington Capital.
61. Mr. PARR, Pittsburgh Post.
62. Mrs. G. W. THOMSON, Journal.

132

THE COMMISSIONERS.

United States Senators.
1. — Ohio.
2. — Delaware.
3. — New Jersey.
4. — Indiana.
5. — Vermont.

Associate Justices of the Supreme Court of the United States.
6. — Pennsylvania.
7. — Iowa.
8. President of the Commission. — Maine.
9. — California.
10. — New Jersey.

Members of the House of Representatives.
11. — Ohio.
12. — Virginia.
13. — Massachusetts.
14. — Ohio.
15. — Massachusetts.

16. U.S. Sen. / U.S. — New York.

Substitute for Allen G. Thurman during his illness.

17. WILLIAM WINDOM, Senator, Minnesota.
18. W. W. CORCORAN.
19. JOHN J. INGALLS, Senator, Kansas.
20. I. C. S. BLACKBURN, Member of Congress, Kentucky.
21. JOHN H. REAGAN, Member of Congress, Texas.
22. B. E. CATTIN, Assistant Secretary Senate.
23. GEORGE A. HOWARD, Assistant Secretary Electoral Com.
24. JAMES H. McKENNEY, Secretary Electoral Commission.
25. JOHN SHERMAN, Senator, Ohio.
26. SAMUEL SHELLABARGER, Counsel for Hayes.
27. WILLIAM F. COOPER, Page to Electoral Commission.
28. D. MURPHY, Stenographer Electoral Commission.
29. GEORGE W. McCRARY, M. C., Ia., and counsel for Hayes.
30. MORRISON R. WAITE, Chief Justice, U.S.S.C.
31. JOHN G. THOMPSON, Sergeant-at-Arms, H.R.
32. JOHN J. NICOLAY, Marshall, U.S.S.C.
33. W. H. REARDON, Marshall, Electoral Commission.
34. E. P. CORVAIZIER, Messenger, U.S. Senate.
35. MRS. Z. CHANDLER.
36. MISS G. A. BOUTWELL.
37. JOHN R. FRENCH, Sergeant-at-Arms, U.S. Senate.
38. MISS G. F. TUCKER.
39. MRS. CHARLES E. HOOKER.
40. MISS CAROLINE BRADLEY.
41.
42. MISS LIDA MILLER.
43. MISS JULIA D. STRONG.
44. PROF. JOSEPH HENRY, Smithsonian Institution.
45. CHARLES G. WILLIAMS, Member of Congress, Wisconsin.
46. MRS. S. VIRGINIA FIELD.
47. MRS. MARY A. MATTHEWS.
48. MRS. RUTH A. HOAR.
49. MRS. CHAPMAN COLEMAN.
50. HAMILTON FISH, Secretary of State.
51. MRS. JULIA K. FISH.
52. MRS. MYRA CLARK GAINES.
53. MRS. JULIA G. TYLER, (Widow of President John Tyler.)
54. MRS. I. V. SWEARINGEN.
55. MRS. VIRGINIA M. WILSON.
56. MRS. RACHAEL H. STRONG.
57. CHARLES GORDON.
58. MRS. IMOGENE R. MORRELL.
59. MRS. JEAN M. LANDER.
60. MISS KATHERINE LEE BAYARD.
61. JOHN J. PATTERSON, Senator, South Carolina.
62. MRS. CATHERINE HARDENBERGH.
63. JOHN H. FLAGG, Legislative Clerk, U.S. Senate.
64. JOHN HITZ, Consul General of Switzerland.
65. CHARLES PAGE BRYAN.
66. GEORGE M. ADAMS, Clerk, House of Representatives.
67. HORATIO KING.
68. S. W. DORSEY, Senator, Arkansas.
69. M. B. BRADY.
70. AMBROSE E. BURNSIDE, Senator, Rhode Island.
71. GEORGE C. GORHAM, Secretary, U.S. Senate.
72. SAMUEL J. RANDALL, Speaker, House of Representatives.
73. F. M. COCKRELL, Senator, Missouri.
74. J. PROCTOR KNOTT, Member of Congress, Kentucky.
75. JOHN B. CLARK, Jr., Member of Congress, Missouri.
76. H. B. ANTHONY, Senator, Rhode Island.
77. BAINBRIDGE WADLEIGH, Senator, New Hampshire.
78. BENJAMIN H. HILL, Senator, Georgia.
79. FERNANDO WOOD, Member of Congress, New York.
80. A. C. HARMER, Member of Congress, Pa.
81. ANNANIAS HERBERT, Messenger, U.S. Supreme Court.
82. G. A. CLARK, Doorkeeper, U.S. Supreme Court.
83. AUGUSTUS W. CUTLER, Member of Congress, New Jersey.
84. A. R. SHEPHERD.
85. S. L. PHELPS, Commissioner, District of Columbia.
86. J. W. POWELL, United States Survey.
87. S. A. HURLBUT, M. C., Ia., and counsel for Hayes.
88. JOHN A. KASSON, M. C., Ia., and counsel for Hayes.
89. GEORGE W. CHILDS.
90. JAMES L. ANDEM, Reporter for N.Y. Asso. Press.
91. STANLEY MATTHEWS, Counsel for Hayes.
92. MRS. J. A. GARFIELD.
93. GEORGE M. ROBESON, Secretary of Navy.
94. ALPHONSO M. TAFT, Secretary of War.
95. BELVA M. LOCKWOOD.
96. GEORGE S. BOUTWELL, Senator, Massachusetts.
97. AARON A. SARGENT, Senator, California.
98. DR. PETER PARKER.
99. JAMES O. WOODRUFF, Scientific Expedition.
100. EUGENE HALE, Member of Congress, Maine.
101. CHARLES FOSTER, Member of Congress, Ohio.
102. JOHN H. MITCHELL, Senator, Oregon.
103. W. P. LYNDE, Member of Congress, Wisconsin.
104. JOHN C. S. ATKINS, Member of Congress, Tennessee.
105. A. A. HARDENBERGH, Member of Congress, New Jersey.
106. THOMAS EWING, Member of Congress, Ohio.
107. WILLIAM E. CHANDLER, Counsel for Hayes.
108. JAMES P. ROOT, Counsel for Hayes.
109. JAMES N. TYNER, Postmaster General.
110. WILLIAM LAWRENCE, M. C., Ohio, counsel for Hayes.
111. D. T. CORBIN.
112. C. D. DRAKE, Chief Justice, U.S. C. of Claims.
113. CHARLES W. JONES, Senator, Florida.
114. P. PHILLIPS.
115. SAUNDERS W. JOHNSTON.
116. N. P. BANKS, Member of Congress, Massachusetts.
117. J. G. CANNON, Member of Congress, Illinois.
118. FLORA FASSETT.
119. ELIZABETH B. JOHNSTON.
120. W. A. J. SPARKS, Member of Congress, Illinois.
121. FREDERICK DOUGLASS.
122. WILLIAM M. EVARTS, Counsel for Hayes.
123. EDWIN W. STOUGHTON, Counsel for Hayes.
124. ZACHARIAH CHANDLER, Secretary of the Interior.
125. ABRAM S. HEWITT, Member of Congress, New York.
126. AMERICUS V. RICE, Member of Congress, Ohio.
127. MRS. CELIA S. SHERMAN.
128. MRS. JENNIE B. BRYAN.
129. MRS. SUSAN M. EDMUNDS.
130. MRS. E. V. MILLER.
131. WILLIAM D. KELLEY, Member of Congress, Pennsylvania.
132. MRS. MARY CLEMMER.
133. CHARLES O'CONOR, Counsel for Tilden.
134. RICHARD T. MERRICK, Counsel for Tilden.
135. GEORGE A. JENKS, M. C., Pa., and counsel for Tilden.
136. W. H. FORNEY, Member of Congress, Alabama.
137. J. RANDOLPH TUCKER, M. C., Va., and counsel for Tilden.
138. TIMOTHY O. HOWE, Sen., Wis., and counsel for Hayes.
139. HENRY WATTERSON, Member of Congress, Kentucky.
140. MRS. ELLEN F. WINDOM.
141. THOMAS B. BRYAN.
142. HIRAM P. BELL, Member of Congress, Georgia.
143. L. Q. C. LAMAR, Member of Congress, Mississippi.
144. HANNIBAL HAMLIN, Senator, Maine.
145. GEORGE BANCROFT, Historian.
146. JUSTIN S. MORRILL, Senator, Vermont.
147. JOHN I. CAMPBELL, Counsel for Tilden.
148. ROSCOE CONKLING, Senator, New York.
149. MONTGOMERY BLAIR, Counsel for Tilden.
150. MATT W. RANSOM, Senator, North Carolina.
151. DAVID DUDLEY FIELD, M. C., N.Y., counsel for Tilden.
152. WILLIAM C. WHITNEY, Counsel for Hayes.
153. THOMAS W. FERRY, President pro Tempore, U.S. Senate.
154. JAMES H. BLOUNT, Member of Congress, Georgia.
155. J. D. CAMERON, Senator, Pennsylvania.
156. MARTIN I. TOWNSEND, Member of Congress, New York.
157. WILLIAM M. SPRINGER, Member of Congress, Illinois.
158. LYMAN TRUMBULL, Counsel for Tilden.
159. MATT H. CARPENTER, Counsel for Tilden.
160. JEREMIAH S. BLACK, Counsel for Tilden.
161. GEORGE HOADLY, Counsel for Tilden.
162. ASHABEL GREEN, Counsel for Tilden.
163. MATTHEW G. EMERY.
164. ALEX. PORTER MORSE, Counsel for Tilden.
165. H. B. BANNING, Member of Congress, Ohio.
166. MRS. NANNIE MERRICK.
167. BLANCHE K. BRUCE, Senator, Mississippi.
168. HENRY W. BLAIR, Member of Congress, New Hampshire.
169. MISS M. Y. FRELINGHUYSEN.
170. MISS CHRISTINE TYNER.
171. SIR EDWARD THORNTON, British Minister.
172. HIESTER CLYMER, Member of Congress, Pennsylvania.
173. MRS. LAURA H. TUCKER.
174. MRS. FANNIE H. GORDON.
175. JOHN B. GORDON, Senator, Georgia.
176. JOHN A. LOGAN, Senator, Illinois.
177. S. S. COX, Member of Congress, New York.
178. MARY F. WAITE.
179. MRS. HELEN M. DORSEY.
180. THOMAS SWAN, Member of Congress, Maryland.
181. MRS. MARY CAMERON.
182. MRS. C. ADELE FASSETT.
183. MRS. MARY A. RICE.
184. JAMES G. BLAINE, Senator, Maine.
185. MRS. SALLIE R. KNOTT.
186. CARLILE P. PATTERSON, Superintendent U.S. Coast Survey.
187. MRS. C. P. PATTERSON.
188. MRS. MARY M. GIBSON.
189. W. B. ALLISON, Senator, Iowa.
190. RANDALL LEE GIBSON, Member of Congress, Louisiana.
191. MRS. LILLIE E. WILLIS.
192. CHARLES W. HOFFMAN, Librarian of Law Library, U.S.S.C.
193. C. H. McCALL, Page, Supreme Court U.S.
194. ROBERT BROWN, Page, Supreme Court U.S.
195. FRED. M. MATTERSON, Page, Supreme Court U.S.
196. H. J. LAUCK, Messenger, Electoral Commission.

GENERAL MARION INVITING A BRITISH OFFICER TO SHARE HIS MEAL
Painting by John Blake White.
Located in Senate wing, third floor, south corridor.

LEIV EIRIKSSON DISCOVERS AMERICA, A.D. 1000
Painting by Per Krohg after original by Christian Krohg.
Location: Senate wing, third floor, east corridor.

MISS MOTT DIRECTING GENERALS MARION AND LEE TO BURN HER MANSION
TO DISLODGE THE BRITISH
Painting by John Blake White.
Location: Senate wing, third floor, south corridor.

Neg. No. 24319

NIAGARA FALLS IN WINTER
Painting by Regis Gignoux.
Location: Senate wing, third floor, south corridor.

Neg. No. 25389

RECALL OF COLUMBUS
Painting by Augustus G. Heaton.
Location: Senate wing, third floor, east corridor.

SERGEANTS JASPER AND NEWTON RESCUING AMERICAN PRISONERS FROM THE BRITISH
Painting by John Blake White.
Location: Senate wing, third floor, south corridor.

Neg. No. 23934

FIVE PAINTINGS LOCATED IN THE HOUSE WING OF THE CAPITOL

DISCOVERY OF THE HUDSON RIVER, by Albert Bierstadt. Acquired by purchase in 1875; located in House wing, Members' private stairway, east.

ENTRANCE INTO MONTEREY, by Albert Bierstadt. Acquired by purchase in 1878; located in House wing, Members' private stairway, west.

SCENE AT THE SIGNING OF THE CONSTITUTION OF THE UNITED STATES, by Howard Chandler Christy. Acquired by purchase in 1940, under authority of Public Resolution 11, Seventy-sixth Congress; located in House wing, east stairway.

WESTWARD THE COURSE OF EMPIRE TAKES ITS WAY, by Emanuel Leutze. Acquired by purchase in 1862; located in House wing, west stairway.

UNITED STATES CAPITOL EXTENSION, oil painting by Robert Kirwan. Presented as a gift from the Chesapeake and Potomac Telephone Company to the United States Government, Office of the Architect of the Capitol in 1961. Located in the formal office of the Speaker of the House of Representatives, Room H–210. (No illustration.)

DISCOVERY OF THE HUDSON RIVER
Painting by Albert Bierstadt.
Location: House wing, Members' private stairway, east.

Neg. No. 269

138

ENTRANCE INTO MONTEREY
Painting by Albert Bierstadt.
Location: House wing, Members' private stairway, west.

SCENE AT THE SIGNING OF THE CONSTITUTION OF THE UNITED STATES

Painting by Howard Chandler Christy.

Location: House wing, east stairway.

Scene at the Signing of the Constitution of the United States

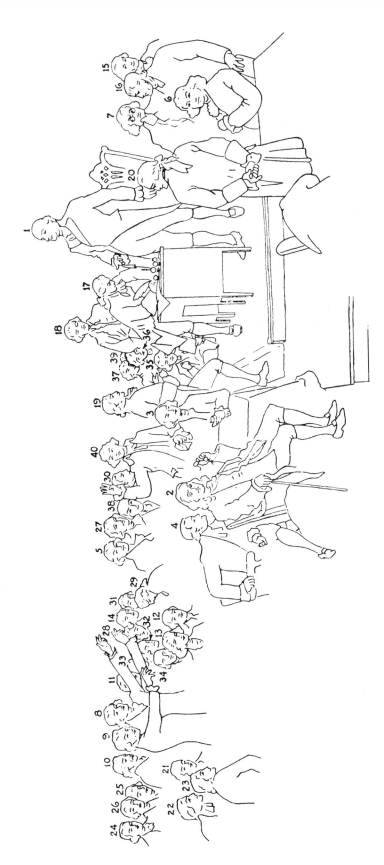

1. Washington, George, Va.
2. Franklin, Benjamin, Pa.
3. Madison, James, Va.
4. Hamilton, Alexander, N.Y.
5. Morris, Gouverneur, Pa.
6. Morris, Robert, Pa.
7. Wilson, James, Pa.
8. Pinckney, Chas. Cotesworth, S.C.
9. Pinckney, Chas., S.C.
10. Rutledge, John, S.C.

11. Butler, Pierce, S.C.
12. Sherman, Roger, Conn.
13. Johnson, William Samuel, Conn.
14. McHenry, James, Md.
15. Read, George, Del.
16. Bassett, Richard, Del.
17. Spaight, Richard Dobbs, N.C.
18. Blount, William, N.C.
19. Williamson, Hugh, N.C.
20. Jenifer, Daniel of St. Thomas, Md.

21. King, Rufus, Mass.
22. Gorham, Nathaniel, Mass.
23. Dayton, Jonathan, N.J.
24. Carroll, Daniel, Md.
25. Few, William, Ga.
26. Baldwin, Abraham, Ga.
27. Langdon, John, N.H.
28. Gilman, Nicholas, N.H.
29. Livingston, William, N.J.
30. Paterson, William, N.J.

31. Mifflin, Thomas, Pa.
32. Clymer, George, Pa.
33. FitzSimons, Thomas, Pa.
34. Ingersoll, Jared, Pa.
35. Bedford, Gunning, Jr., Del.
36. Brearley, David, N.J.
37. Dickinson, John, Del.
38. Blair, John, Va.
39. Broom, Jacob, Del.
40. Jackson, William (Secretary)

141

WESTWARD THE COURSE OF EMPIRE TAKES ITS WAY
Painting by Emanuel Leutze.
Location: House wing, west staircase.

EIGHTEEN PAINTINGS LOCATED IN THE CENTRAL SECTION OF THE CAPITOL

UNITED STATES CAPITOL, water color by Hughson Hawley; located in the corridor outside the Office of the Architect of the Capitol. Acquired by purchase in 1905. (No illustration.)

Seventeen paintings of forts, by Brigadier General Seth Eastman, located in west corridor, first floor, central section of Capitol.

These historic paintings represent the principal fortifications of the United States during the period of the 1870's—General Eastman receiving $100 per month for his services in addition to his pay as a retired officer of the Army. General Eastman started on this work in 1870 and he completed the 17 paintings by 1875. The following forts are represented:

Fort Knox, Maine.
Fort Taylor, Florida.
Fort Snelling, Minnesota.
Fort Scammel and Fort Gorges, Maine.
Fort Defiance, New Mexico (now located in Arizona).
Fort Sumter, South Carolina (before the war).
Fort Sumter, South Carolina (after the bombardment).
Fort Sumter, South Carolina (after the war).
Fort Mackinac, Michigan.
Fort Mifflin, Pennsylvania.
Fort Lafayette, New York.
Fort Tompkins and Fort Wadsworth, New York.
Fort West Point, New York.
Fort Delaware, Delaware.
Fort Jefferson, Florida.
Fort Trumbull, Connecticut.
Fort Rice, North Dakota.

FORT DEFIANCE, New Mexico (now located in Arizona)
Painting by Seth Eastman.
Location: west corridor, first floor, central section of the Capitol.

Neg. No. 24110

FORT DELAWARE, Delaware
Painting by Seth Eastman.
Location: west corridor, first floor, central section of the Capitol.

144

FORT JEFFERSON, Florida
Painting by Seth Eastman.
Location: west corridor, first floor, central section of the Capitol.

FORT KNOX, Maine
Painting by Seth Eastman.
Location: west corridor, first floor, central section of the Capitol.

FORT LAFAYETTE, New York
Painting by Seth Eastman.
Location: west corridor, first floor, central section of the Capitol.

147

FORT MACKINAC, Michigan
Painting by Seth Eastman.
Location: west corridor, first floor, central section of the Capitol.

148

FORT MIFFLIN, Pennsylvania
Painting by Seth Eastman.
Location: west corridor, first floor, central section of the Capitol.

Neg. No. 24898

149

FORT RICE, North Dakota
Painting by Seth Eastman.
Location: west corridor, first floor, central section of the Capitol.

FORT SCAMMEL and FORT GORGES, Maine
Painting by Seth Eastman.
Location: west corridor, first floor, central section of the Capitol.

FORT SNELLING, Minnesota
Painting by Seth Eastman.
Location: west corridor, first floor, central section of the Capitol.

FORT SUMTER, South Carolina (before the war)
Painting by Seth Eastman.
Location: west corridor, first floor, central section of the Capitol.

153

Neg. No. 24107

FORT SUMTER, South Carolina (after the bombardment)
Painting by Seth Eastman.
Location: west corridor, first floor, central section of the Capitol.

154

FORT SUMTER, South Carolina (after the war)
Painting by Seth Eastman.
Location: west corridor, first floor, central section of the Capitol.

155

FORT TAYLOR, Florida
Painting by Seth Eastman.
Location: west corridor, first floor, central section of the Capitol.

Neg. No. 24902

156

Neg. No. 24903

FORT TOMPKINS and FORT WADSWORTH, New York
Painting by Seth Eastman.
Location: west corridor, first floor, central section of the Capitol.

157

FORT TRUMBULL, Connecticut
Painting by Seth Eastman.
Location: west corridor, first floor, central section of the Capitol.

FORT WEST POINT, New York
Painting by Seth Eastman.
Location: west corridor, first floor, central section of the Capitol.

Neg. No. 24104

159

TEN PAINTINGS LOCATED IN THE HOUSE OFFICE BUILDINGS

Nine Paintings of Indian Scenes, by Brigadier General Seth Eastman

These paintings were executed by General Eastman in the late 1860's under a special commission directing him to make these paintings for the House Indian Affairs Committee room, at that time, and for many years thereafter, located in the Capitol Building. They were transferred to the House Office Building in 1945 when that committee (renamed Interior and Insular Affairs in the 80th Congress) moved from the Capitol to the Longworth House Office Building, Room 1324.

The scenes represented are as follows:

BUFFALO CHASE
DEATH WHOOP
DOG DANCE OF THE DAKOTAS
FEEDING THE DEAD
THE INDIAN COUNCIL
INDIAN MODE OF TRAVELING
INDIAN WOMAN DRESSING A DEER SKIN
RICE GATHERERS
SPEARING FISH IN WINTER

One Painting, Peace

PEACE, by Walter Dean; placed in Capitol in 1900; acquired by purchase in 1928; located in the Armed Services Committee Room in the Cannon House Office Building, Room 313. (No illustration.)

BUFFALO CHASE
Painting by Seth Eastman.
Location: Longworth House Office Building.

Neg. No. 698

DEATH WHOOP
Painting by Seth Eastman.
Location: Longworth House Office Building.

161

DOG DANCE OF THE DAKOTAS
Painting by Seth Eastman.
Location: Longworth House Office Building.

FEEDING THE DEAD
Painting by Seth Eastman.
Location: Longworth House Office Building.

THE INDIAN COUNCIL
Painting by Seth Eastman.
Location: Longworth House Office Building.

164

INDIAN MODE OF TRAVELING
Painting by Seth Eastman.
Location: Longworth House Office Building.

165

INDIAN WOMAN DRESSING A DEER SKIN
Painting by Seth Eastman.
Location: Longworth House Office Building.

166

RICE GATHERERS
Painting by Seth Eastman.
Location: Longworth House Office Building.

SPEARING FISH IN WINTER
Painting by Seth Eastman.
Location: Longworth House Office Building.

ONE PAINTING LOCATED IN THE OLD SENATE OFFICE BUILDING

BRIDES OF VENICE, by J. H. Van Lerius; a gift from the daughters of Mrs. Alice Pike Barney in 1934; located in the Old Senate Office Building Storeroom.

BRIDES OF VENICE
Painting by J. H. Van Lerius.
Location: Old Senate Office Building Storeroom.

Marble and Bronze Busts Located in the United States Capitol

PRESIDENTS OF THE UNITED STATES
Seven Busts

JOHN QUINCY ADAMS, marble bust by John Crookshanks King; acquired in 1849 (records incomplete); located in House wing, second floor, Congressional Ladies Retiring Room, H–235, formerly the Office of the Clerk of the House, earlier the Office of the Speaker of the House, the room in which Mr. Adams died.

ABRAHAM LINCOLN, marble bust by Sarah Fisher Ames; acquired by purchase in 1868; located in Senate wing, third floor, east corridor.

ABRAHAM LINCOLN, marble head by Gutzon Borglum; accepted by the Joint Committee on the Library as a gift from Eugene Meyer, Jr., in 1908; located in the Rotunda.

WILLIAM McKINLEY JR., bronze bust by Emma Cadwalader-Guild; acquired by purchase in 1903; located in the President's Room, Senate wing, second floor, Room S–216.

ZACHARY TAYLOR, marble bust (sculptor unknown); acquired by purchase in 1909; located in Senate wing, third floor, east.

GEORGE WASHINGTON, bronze bust by David d'Angers; accepted as a gift from the French Nation in 1905; replacing a similar bust destroyed by fire in 1851; located in the Rotunda.

GEORGE WASHINGTON, marble bust, reproduced from the original sandstone bust, which was executed by Antonio Capellano in 1827. From the plaster model, as executed by G. Giannetti in 1959–1960, the reproduction was carved in marble by the carvers of the Vermont Marble Company, under the supervision of Paul Manship, for the Extended East Front of the Capitol. The bust is in the center of the panel, "Fame and Peace Crowning Washington," located above the Rotunda Bronze Doors on the East Central Portico.

Neg. No. 16756
JOHN QUINCY ADAMS
Bust by John Crookshanks King.
Location: House wing, second floor, Congressional Ladies Retiring Room H–235. Formerly the Office of the Clerk of the House of Representatives.

Neg. No. 200
ABRAHAM LINCOLN
Bust by Sarah Fisher Ames.
Location: Senate wing, third floor, east corridor.

ABRAHAM LINCOLN
Head by Gutzon Borglum.
Location: Rotunda

WILLIAM McKINLEY
Bronze bust by Emma Cadwalader-Guild.
Location: President's Room, second floor, Senate wing.

ZACHARY TAYLOR
Bust by unknown artist.
Location: Senate wing, third floor, east.

GEORGE WASHINGTON
Bust by David d'Angers.
Location: Rotunda.

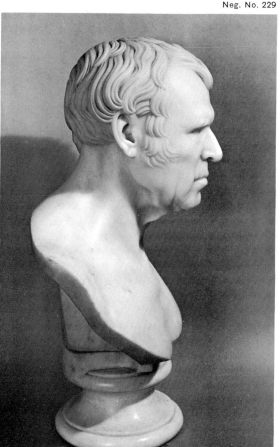

FAME AND PEACE CROWNING GEORGE WASHINGTON
Bust and Relief—original sandstone by Antonio Capellano.
Plaster model executed by G. Giannetti and carved in marble by the carvers of the Vermont Marble Company
all under the supervision of Paul Manship.
Location: above the Rotunda Bronze Door, East Central Portico.

Neg. No. 20418

VICE PRESIDENTS OF THE UNITED STATES
Thirty-five Busts

Thirty-five marble busts of Vice Presidents—acquired under authority of Senate resolutions of January 27, 1885, May 13, 1886, January 6, 1898, and March 28, 1947.

This collection includes all Vice Presidents from the first Vice President, John Adams, through Alben W. Barkley; 20 of these busts are located in niches in the gallery walls of the Senate Chamber, 12 in the second floor corridors of the Senate wing adjacent to the Chamber, 1 in the Vice President's formal office, S–214, and 2 in the Senate Reception Room, S–213, adjacent to the Senate lobby.

NAME	STATE	PERIOD OF SERVICE	SCULPTOR	DATE OF PURCHASE
*John Adams [1]	Massachusetts	Apr. 30, 1789–Mar. 3, 1797	Daniel Chester French	1890
Thomas Jefferson [1]	Virginia	Mar. 4, 1797–Mar. 3, 1801	Sir Moses Ezekiel	1889
Aaron Burr [1]	New York	Mar. 4, 1801–Mar. 3, 1805	Jacques Jouvenal	1893
George Clinton [1]	New York	Mar. 4, 1805–Apr. 20, 1812	Vittorio A. Ciani	1894
Elbridge Gerry [1]	Massachusetts	Mar. 4, 1813–Nov. 23, 1814	Herbert Adams	1892
Daniel D. Tompkins [1]	New York	Mar. 4, 1817–Mar. 3, 1825	Charles H. Niehaus	1891
John C. Calhoun [1]	South Carolina	Mar. 4, 1825–Dec. 28, 1832	Theodore A. Mills	1896
Martin Van Buren [1]	New York	Mar. 4, 1833–Mar. 3, 1837	U. S. J. Dunbar	1891
Richard M. Johnson [1]	Kentucky	Mar. 4, 1837–Mar. 3, 1841	James P. Voorhees	1895
John Tyler [1]	Virginia	Mar. 4, 1841–Apr. 4, 1841	William C. McCauslen	1898
George M. Dallas [1]	Pennsylvania	Mar. 4, 1845–Mar. 3, 1849	Henry J. Ellicott	1893
Millard Fillmore [1]	New York	Mar. 5, 1849–July 9, 1850	Robert Cushing	1895
William R. King [1]	Alabama	Mar. 4, 1853–Apr. 18, 1853	William C. McCauslen	1896
John C. Breckinridge [1]	Kentucky	Mar. 4, 1857–Mar. 3, 1861	James P. Voorhees	1896
Hannibal Hamlin [1]	Maine	Mar. 4, 1861–Mar. 3, 1865	Franklin Simmons	1889

See footnotes at end of table.

171

NAME	STATE	PERIOD OF SERVICE	SCULPTOR	DATE OF PUR-CHASE
Andrew Johnson [1]	Tennessee	Mar. 4, 1865–Apr. 15, 1865	William C. McCauslen	1900
Schuyler Colfax [1]	Indiana	Mar. 4, 1869–Mar. 3, 1873	Frances M. Goodwin	1897
Henry Wilson [2,6]	Massachusetts	Mar. 4, 1873–Nov. 22, 1875	Daniel Chester French	1885–86
William A. Wheeler [1]	New York	Mar. 5, 1877–Mar. 3, 1881	Edward C. Potter	1892
Chester A. Arthur [1]	New York	Mar. 4, 1881–Sept. 19, 1881	Augustus Saint-Gaudens	1892
Thomas A. Hendricks [1]	Indiana	Mar. 4, 1885–Nov. 25, 1885	U. S. J. Dunbar	1890
Levi P. Morton [3]	New York	Mar. 4, 1889–Mar. 3, 1893	F. Edwin Elwell	1891
Adlai E. Stevenson [3]	Illinois	Mar. 4, 1893–Mar. 3, 1897	Franklin Simmons	1894
Garret A. Hobart [3]	New Jersey	Mar. 4, 1897–Nov. 21, 1899	F. Edwin Elwell	1901
Theodore Roosevelt [3]	New York	Mar. 4, 1901–Sept. 14, 1901	James Earle Fraser	1910
Charles W. Fairbanks [3]	Indiana	Mar. 4, 1905–Mar. 3, 1909	Franklin Simmons	1909
James S. Sherman [3]	New York	Mar. 4, 1909–Oct. 30, 1912	Bessie Potter Vonnoh	1912
Thomas R. Marshall [4]	Indiana	Mar. 4, 1913–Mar. 3, 1921	Moses A. Wainer Dykaar	1920
Calvin Coolidge [4]	Massachusetts	Mar. 4, 1921–Aug. 2, 1923	Moses A. Wainer Dykaar	1929
Charles G. Dawes [4]	Illinois	Mar. 4, 1925–Mar. 3, 1929	Jo Davidson	1935
Charles Curtis [4]	Kansas	Mar. 4, 1929–Mar. 3, 1933	Moses A. Wainer Dykaar	1935
John Nance Garner [5]	Texas	Mar. 4, 1933–Jan. 20, 1941	James Earle Fraser	1943
Henry A. Wallace [5]	Iowa	Jan. 20, 1941–Jan. 20, 1945	Jo Davidson	1948
Harry S. Truman [4]	Missouri	Jan. 20, 1945–Apr. 12, 1945	Charles Keck	1947
Alben W. Barkley [3]	Kentucky	Jan. 20, 1949–Jan. 20, 1953	Kalervo Kallio	1958

Note:

*On April 21, the Vice-President-elect first appeared in and addressed the Senate. The oath of office was administered to John Adams on June 3, 1789. (Senate Journal, Vol. 1, pages 16, 31.)

[1] Located in the Senate Chamber, gallery.

[2] Located in the Vice President's formal office, Room S–214.

[3] Located in the Senate wing, second floor, main corridor.

[4] Located in the Senate wing, second floor, east corridor.

[5] Located in the Senate Reception Room, adjacent to the Senate lobby.

[6] Henry Wilson legally changed his name at age 21 from Jeremiah Jones Colbaith.

JOHN ADAMS, Vice President of the United States

Bust by Daniel C. French.
Location: Senate Chamber, gallery.

Neg. No. 25720

CHESTER A. ARTHUR, Vice President of the United States

Bust by Augustus Saint-Gaudens.
Location: Senate Chamber, gallery.

Neg. No. 25721

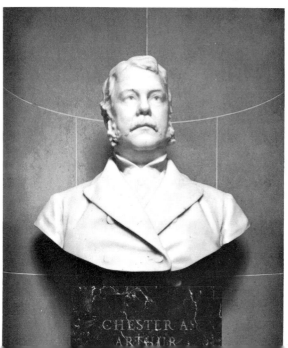

ALBEN W. BARKLEY, Vice President of the
United States
Bust by Kalervo Kallio.
Location: Senate Wing, second floor, main corridor.

JOHN C. BRECKENRIDGE,[1] Vice President of the
United States
Bust by James P. Voorhees.
Location: Senate Chamber, gallery.

[1] The correct spelling of the name is BRECKINRIDGE.

AARON BURR, Vice President of the United States

Bust by Jacques Jouvenal.
Location: Senate Chamber, gallery.

JOHN C. CALHOUN, Vice President of the United
States
Bust by Theodore A. Mills.
Location: Senate Chamber, gallery.

GEORGE CLINTON, Vice President of the United
States
Bust by Vittorio A. Ciani.
Location: Senate Chamber, gallery.

SCHUYLER COLFAX, Vice President of the United
States
Bust by Frances M. Goodwin.
Location: Senate Chamber, gallery.

CALVIN COOLIDGE, Vice President of the United
States
Bust by Moses A. Wainer Dykaar.
Location: Senate wing, second floor, east corridor.

CHARLES CURTIS, Vice President of the United States
Bust by Moses A. Wainer Dykaar.
Location: Senate wing, second floor, east corridor.

GEORGE M. DALLAS, Vice President of the United States
Bust by Henry J. Ellicott.
Location: Senate Chamber, gallery.

CHARLES G. DAWES, Vice President of the United States
Bust by Jo Davidson.
Location: Senate wing, second floor, east corridor.

CHARLES W. FAIRBANKS, Vice President of the United States
Bust by Franklin Simmons.
Location: Senate wing, second floor, main corridor.

MILLARD FILLMORE, Vice President of the United States
Bust by Robert Cushing.
Location: Senate Chamber, gallery.

JOHN N. GARNER, Vice President of the United States
Bust by James Earle Fraser.
Location: Senate Reception Room, adjacent to the Senate lobby.

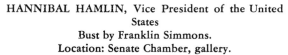

ELBRIDGE GERRY, Vice President of the United States
Bust by Herbert Adams.
Location: Senate Chamber, gallery.

HANNIBAL HAMLIN, Vice President of the United States
Bust by Franklin Simmons.
Location: Senate Chamber, gallery.

THOMAS A. HENDRICKS, Vice President of the United States
Bust by U. S. J. Dunbar.
Location: Senate Chamber, gallery.

GARRET A. HOBART, Vice President of the United
States
Bust by F. Edwin Elwell.
Location: Senate wing, second floor, main corridor.

THOMAS JEFFERSON, Vice President of the United
States
Bust by Sir Moses Ezekiel.
Location: Senate Chamber, gallery.

ANDREW JOHNSON, Vice President of the United
States
Bust by William C. McCauslen.
Location: Senate Chamber, gallery.

RICHARD M. JOHNSON, Vice President of the United
States
Bust by James P. Voorhees.
Location: Senate Chamber, gallery.

Neg. No. 25735

WILLIAM R. KING, Vice President of the United
States
Bust by William C. McCauslen.
Location: Senate Chamber, gallery.

Neg. No. 25749

THOMAS R. MARSHALL, Vice President of the United
States
Bust by Moses A. Wainer Dykaar.
Location: Senate wing, second floor, east corridor.

LEVI P. MORTON, Vice President of the United States
Bust by F. Edwin Elwell.
Location: Senate wing, second floor, main corridor.

Neg. No. 25750

THEODORE ROOSEVELT, Vice President of the
United States
Bust by James Earle Fraser.
Location: Senate wing, second floor, main corridor.

Neg. No. 25751

178

JAMES S. SHERMAN, Vice Persident of the United
States
Bust by Bessie Potter Vonnoh.
Location: Senate wing, second floor, main corridor.

ADLAI E. STEVENSON, Vice President of the United
States
Bust by Franklin Simmons.
Location: Senate wing, second floor, main corridor.

DANIEL TOMPKINS, Vice President of the United
States
Bust by Charles H. Niehaus.
Location: Senate Chamber, gallery.

HARRY S. TRUMAN, Vice President of the United
States
Bust by Charles Keck.
Location: Senate wing, second floor, east corridor.

Neg. No. 25737

JOHN TYLER, Vice President of the United States
Bust by William C. McCauslen.
Location: Senate Chamber, gallery.

Neg. No. 25738

MARTIN VAN BUREN, Vice President of the United
States
Bust by U. S. J. Dunbar.
Location: Senate Chamber, gallery.

HENRY A. WALLACE, Vice President of the United
States
Bust by Jo Davidson.
Location: Senate Reception Room, adjacent to the
Senate lobby.

Neg. No. 25755

WILLIAM A. WHEELER, Vice President of the United
States
Bust by Edward C. Potter.
Location: Senate Chamber, gallery.

Neg. No. 25739

HENRY WILSON, Vice President of the United States
Bust by Daniel Chester French.
Location: Vice President's formal office.

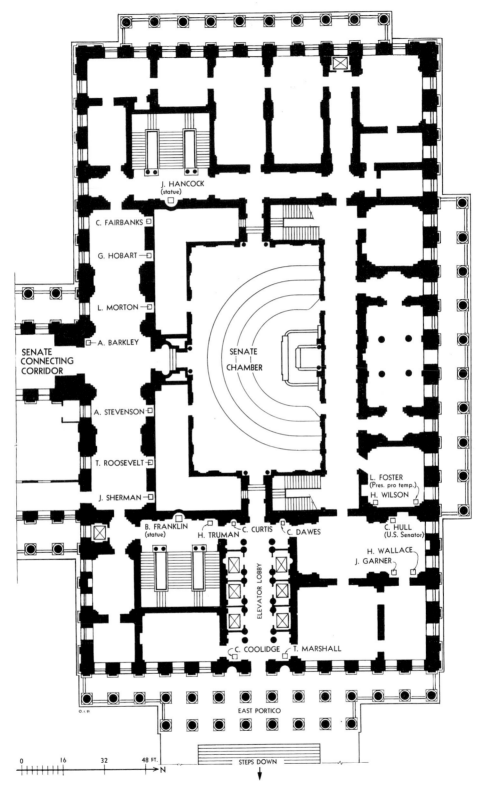

PLAN OF 2D (PRINCIPAL) FLOOR, SENATE WING, SHOWING ARRANGEMENT OF BUSTS OF THE VICE PRESIDENTS AND OTHER STATESMEN.

182

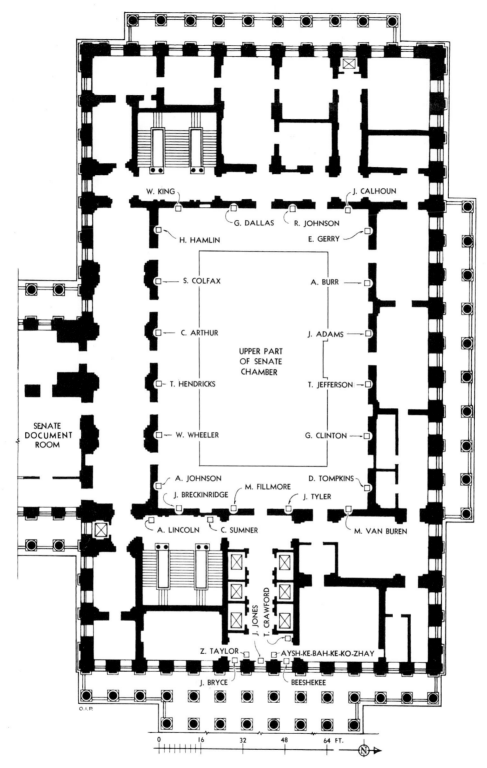

W. KING

J. CALHOUN

G. DALLAS   R. JOHNSON

H. HAMLIN   E. GERRY

S. COLFAX   A. BURR

C. ARTHUR   J. ADAMS

UPPER PART
OF SENATE
CHAMBER

T. HENDRICKS   T. JEFFERSON

SENATE
DOCUMENT
ROOM

W. WHEELER   G. CLINTON

A. JOHNSON   D. TOMPKINS

J. BRECKINRIDGE   M. FILLMORE   J. TYLER

A. LINCOLN   C. SUMNER   M. VAN BUREN

J. JONES
T. CRAWFORD

Z. TAYLOR   AYSH-KE-BAH-KE-KO-ZHAY

J. BRYCE   BEESHEKEE

O.I.P.

0   16   32   48   64 FT.

N

PLAN OF 3D (GALLERY) FLOOR, SENATE WING, SHOWING ARRANGEMENT OF BUSTS OF THE VICE
PRESIDENTS AND OTHERS.

183

PRESIDENT PRO TEMPORE OF THE SENATE

One Bust

One marble bust of Lafayette S. Foster, president pro tempore of the Senate 1865–66 by Charles Calverly.   Accepted by Senate resolution as a gift from Mrs. Foster in 1885; located in Vice President's formal office, S–214.

Neg. No. 25810

LAFAYETTE S. FOSTER, President Pro Tempore of the Senate, 1865–66
Bust by Charles Calverly.
Location: Vice President's formal office.

CHIEF JUSTICES OF THE UNITED STATES

Ten Busts

Ten marble busts of Chief Justices of the United States, acquired under appropriation and other authority—located in Old Supreme Court Chamber, S–228, formerly the Senate Chamber.

CHIEF JUSTICE	PERIOD OF SERVICE AS CHIEF JUSTICE	SCULPTOR	DATE OF PURCHASE
John Jay	1789–1795	John Frazee	1831
John Rutledge	1795–1795	Alexander Galt	1858
Oliver Ellsworth	1796–1800	Hezekiah Augur	1837–44
John Marshall	1801–1835	Hiram Powers	1836
Roger B. Taney	1836–1864	Augustus Saint-Gaudens	1877
Salmon P. Chase	1864–1873	Thomas D. Jones	1875
Morrison R. Waite	1874–1888	Augustus Saint-Gaudens	1875
Melville W. Fuller	1888–1910	William Ordway Partridge	1891
Edward D. White	1910–1921	Bryant Baker	1911
William Howard Taft	1921–1930	Bryant Baker	1934

SALMON P. CHASE, Chief Justice of the United States, 1864–1873
Bust by Thomas D. Jones.
Location: Old Supreme Court Chamber, second floor.
Neg. No. 496

OLIVER ELLSWORTH, Chief Justice of the United States, 1796–1800
Bust by Hezekiah Augur.
Location: Old Supreme Court Chamber, second floor.
Neg. No. 493

Neg. No. 497

MELVILLE W. FULLER, Chief Justice of the United
States, 1888–1910
Bust by William Ordway Partridge.
Location: Old Supreme Court Chamber, second floor.

Neg. No. 196

JOHN JAY, Chief Justice of the United States,
1789–1795
Bust by John Frazee.
Location: Old Supreme Court Chamber, second floor.

JOHN MARSHALL, Chief Justice of the United States,
1801–1835
Bust by Hiram Powers.
Location: Old Supreme Court Chamber, second floor.

Neg. No. 494

JOHN RUTLEDGE, Chief Justice of the United States,
1795–1795
Bust by Alexander Galt.
Location: Old Supreme Court Chamber, second floor.

Neg. No. 492

Neg. No. 24724

WILLIAM HOWARD TAFT, Chief Justice of the United
States, 1921–1930
Bust by Bryant Baker.
Location: Old Supreme Court Chamber, second floor.

Neg. No. 24725

ROGER B. TANEY, Chief Justice of the United States,
1836–1864
Bust by Augustus Saint-Gaudens.
Location: Old Supreme Court Chamber, second floor.

MORRISON R. WAITE, Chief Justice of the United
States, 1874–88
Bust by Augustus Saint-Gaudens.
Location: Old Supreme Court Chamber, second floor.

Neg. No. 498

EDWARD D. WHITE, Chief Justice of the United
States, 1910–1921
Bust by Bryant Baker.
Location: Old Supreme Court Chamber, second floor.

Neg. No. 499

UNITED STATES SENATORS

Three Busts

HENRY CLAY, miniature marble bust by Albert P. Henry; acquired by purchase by the Joint Committee on the Library in 1881; located in the Office of the Architect of the Capitol, Room SB–14.

CORDELL HULL, (also a Representative and Secretary of State), bronze bust by George Conlon; accepted by the Joint Committee on the Library as a gift from the Cumberland, Maryland Evening and Sunday Times, under Senate Concurrent Resolution 56 (78th Congress), agreed to December 4, 1944; located in the Senate Reception Room, S–213 adjoining the Senate lobby.

CHARLES SUMNER, marble bust by Martin Milmore; accepted by the Joint Committee on the Library as a gift from Anna Shaw Curtis, under Senate resolution agreed to January 26, 1894; located in the Senate wing, third floor, east corridor.

Neg. No. 22289

HENRY CLAY
Miniature marble bust by Albert P. Henry.
Location: Office of the Architect of the Capitol.

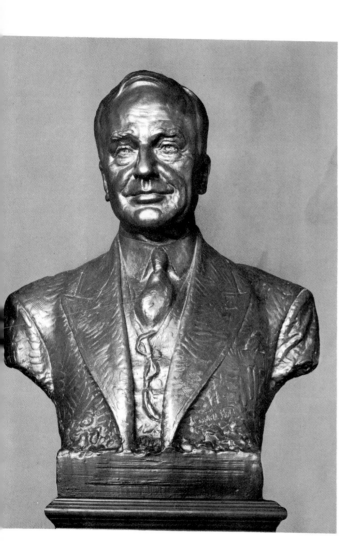

Neg. No. 25748

CORDELL HULL
Bust by George Conlon.
Location: Senators' Reception Room, Senate wing.

Neg. No. 00219

CHARLES SUMNER
Bust by Martin Milmore.
Location: Senate wing, third floor, east
corridor.

SPEAKERS AND MEMBERS OF THE HOUSE OF REPRESENTATIVES

(LOCATED IN THE CANNON HOUSE OFFICE BUILDING ROTUNDA)

Nine Busts

Seven marble portrait busts were removed from the niches in the walls of the galleries of the House Chamber in July, 1949, and transferred to the Rotunda of the Cannon House Office Building due to elimination of the niches under the remodeling of the Chamber program.· The bust of Speaker Cannon was already in the House Office Building. The bust of Speaker Martin was placed in 1962.

SPEAKERS OR MEMBERS	LEGISLATION	UNVEILED OR PLACED	SCULPTOR
Joseph G. Cannon...........	H. RES. 873, 62nd Cong. Acceptance authorized Feb. 28, 1913. The bust of Speaker Cannon was a gift of friends by subscription, which was placed during his lifetime in recognition of his services as Speaker; also his work in securing legislation providing for the Cannon House Office Building and Capitol Power Plant.	1913	Albert Jaegers
James B. (Champ) Clark......	H. RES. 568, 67th Cong. Passed Mar. 1, 1923. The bust of Champ Clark commemorates his service as a Representative from the State of Missouri.	1925	Moses A. Wainer Dykaar
Nicholas Longworth.........	H. RES. 44, 72nd Cong. Dec. 8, 1931. Passed May 27, 1932.	1932	Moses A. Wainer Dykaar
Joseph W. Martin, Jr.........	H. RES. 393, 87th Cong., 1st Session. Passed Sept. 20, 1961. Accepted as a gift of the National Federation of Republican Women.	1962	Suzanne Silvercruys Stevenson
Thomas Brackett Reed.......	H. RES. 315, 76th Cong. Passed Oct. 18, 1939.	1943	Gutzon Borglum, completed by Lincoln Borglum.
Claude Kitchin..............	H. RES. 95, 71st Cong. 2nd Sess. Dec. 13, 1929. Passed Dec. 18, 1929.	1931	Edgardo Simone
Martin B. Madden..........	H. RES. 226, 70th Cong. Passed May 26, 1928.	1929	Albin Polasek
James R. Mann..............	H. RES. 568, 67th Cong. Passed Mar. 1, 1923.	1925	Herbert Adams
Oscar W. Underwood........	H. RES. 55, 72nd Cong. Dec. 14, 1931. Passed May 27, 1932.	1933	Chester Beach

Neg. No. 24683

JOSEPH G. CANNON
Bust by Albert Jaegers.
Location: Rotunda of the Cannon House Office Building.

Neg. No. 24684

JAMES B. (CHAMP) CLARK
Bust by Moses A. Wainer Dykaar.
Location: Rotunda of the Cannon House Office Building.

NICHOLAS LONGWORTH
Bust by Moses A. Wainer Dykaar.
Location: Rotunda of the Cannon House Office Building.

Neg. No. 24686

JOSEPH W. MARTIN, JR.
Bust by Suzanne Silvercruys Stevenson.
Location: Rotunda of the Cannon House Office Building.

Neg. No. 24689

191

THOMAS BRACKETT REED
Bust by Gutzon Borglum, completed by Lincoln Borglum.
Location: Rotunda of the Cannon House Office Building.

CLAUDE KITCHIN
Bust by Edgardo Simone.
Location: Rotunda of the Cannon House Office Building.

MARTIN B. MADDEN
Bust by Albin Polasek.
Location: Rotunda of the Cannon House Office Building.

JAMES R. MANN
Bust by Herbert Adams.
Location: Rotunda of the Cannon House Office Building.

192

OSCAR W. UNDERWOOD
Bust by Chester Beach.
Location: Rotunda of the Cannon House Office Building.

INTERNATIONAL AND OTHER OUTSTANDING FIGURES

Seven Busts

Military and Naval Leaders

GIUSEPPE GARIBALDI, marble bust by Giuseppe Martegana; accepted by the Joint Committee on the Library in 1888 as a gift from members of the Italian Society of Washington, Citizens of Italian descent; located in the lobby of the Old Law Library entrance, opposite room S–141, Senate wing, first floor. Italian patriot and soldier, under whose courageous leadership the unification of Italy was accomplished.

JOHN PAUL JONES, bronze bust executed in 1904 from the original plaster executed from life in 1780 by Antoine Houdon; accepted by the Joint Committee on the Library as a gift from the Secretary of the Navy in 1948; located in the Senate wing, third floor, east. American Naval Officer in the Revolutionary War.

T. (THADDEUS) KOSCIUSZKO, marble bust by H. D. Saunders (Dmochowski); acquired by purchase in 1857; located in the lobby of the Old Law Library entrance, opposite room S–141, Senate wing, first floor. Polish-American patriot and

statesman, who served in the Continental Army during the Revolutionary War.

GENERAL LAFAYETTE, marble bust by David d'Angers; acquired by purchase in 1904 replacing a similar bust acquired by gift from the artist in 1829, destroyed by fire in 1851; located in the Rotunda. French patriot, close personal friend of George Washington and General in the Continental Army during the American Revolution. Entrusted with the defense of Virginia, he was in the place of honor at the moment of victory.

K. K. (CASIMIR) PULASKI, marble bust by H. Dmochowski (Saunders); acquired by purchase in 1882; located in the lobby of the Old Law Library entrance, opposite room S–141, Senate wing, first floor. Polish-American patriot, fought with our armies in the War of the Revolution and earned his rights of American citizenship by giving his life at the siege of Savannah in 1779.

JAMES, VISCOUNT BRYCE, bronze bust by Sir William Reid Dick; accepted by the Joint Committee on the Library as a gift in 1922 from Sir Charles Cheers Wakefield for the Sulgrave Institution of Great Britain; located in the Senate wing, third floor, east. Statesman and Ambassador from Great Britain to the United States.

THOMAS CRAWFORD, marble bust by Tommaso Gagliardi; acquired by purchase in 1871; located in the Senate wing, third floor, east. American sculptor, represented in the United States Capitol by the Statue of Freedom surmounting the Capitol Dome; sculpture of the Pediment, Senate wing, east front; Bronze Doors—House and Senate wings (Doors completed by William Rinehart) and marble statues of Justice and History on the cap above the Bronze Doors of the Senate wing.

Neg. No. 24555

JAMES, VISCOUNT BRYCE
Bust by Sir William Reid Dick.
Location: Senate wing, third floor, east.

Neg. No. 189

THOMAS CRAWFORD
Bust by Tommaso Gagliardi.
Location: Senate wing, third floor, east.

GIUSEPPE GARIBALDI, Italian patriot.
Bust by Giuseppe Martegana.
Located in the Senate wing, first floor area, adjacent to
room S-141.

JOHN PAUL JONES
Bust by Antoine Houdon.
Location: Senate wing, third floor, east.

T. KOSCIUSZKO, Polish-American patriot.
Bust by H. D. Saunders (Dmochowski).
Located in Senate wing, first floor area, adjacent to room
S-141.

GENERAL LAFAYETTE
Bust by David d'Angers.
Location: Rotunda.

K. K. PULASKI, Polish-American patriot.
Bust by H. Dmochowski (Saunders).
Located in Senate wing, first floor area, adjacent to room S–141.

196

INDIAN CHIEF

One Bust

AYSH-KE-BAH-KE-KO-ZHAY, (Flat-Mouth), a Chippewa Chief. Marble bust executed by Francis Vincenti for Capitol in 1858, while employed at Capitol as a sculptor and modeler, located in Senate wing, third floor, east.

Neg. No. 24553

AYSH-KE-BAH-KE-KO-ZHAY (Flat-Mouth)
Bust by Francis Vincenti.
Location: Senate wing, third floor, east.

INDIAN WARRIOR

Two Busts

BEESHEKEE, (Buffalo), a Chippewa warrior. Marble bust executed by Francis Vincenti for Capitol in 1854, while employed at Capitol as a sculptor and modeler; located in Senate wing, third floor, east.

BEESHEKEE, (Buffalo), a Chippewa warrior. Bronze bust (copy of Vincenti's marble bust) executed by Joseph Lassalle for Capitol in 1858, while employed in the bronze shops at the Capitol; located in House wing, at the foot of the grand stairway, west.

BEESHEKEE (Buffalo)
Bust by Francis Vincenti.
Location: Senate wing, third floor, east.
Neg. No. 181B

BEESHEKEE (Buffalo)
Bust by Joseph Lassalle (copy of marble bust by Vincenti).
Location: House wing, at the foot of the grand stairway, west.
Neg. No. 25071

198

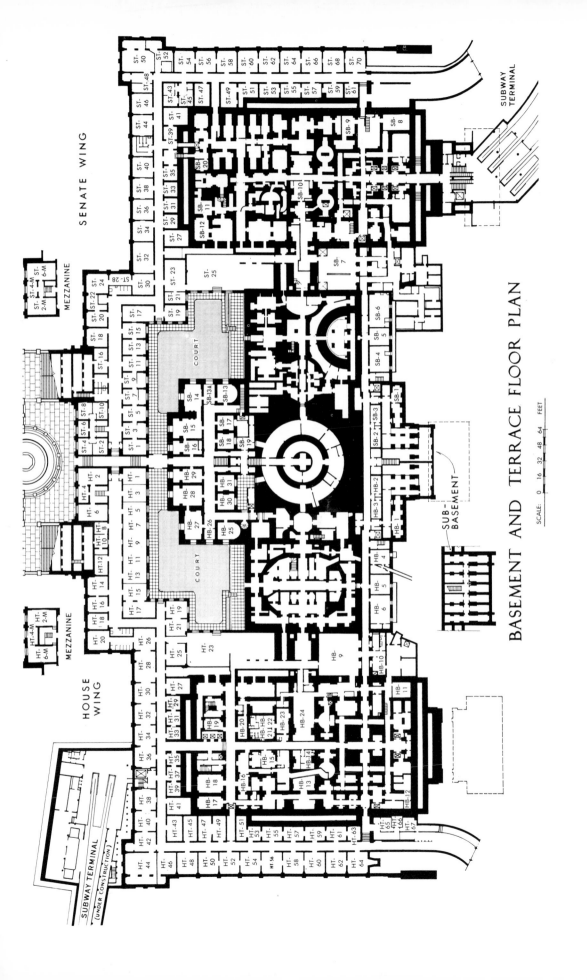

BASEMENT AND TERRACE FLOOR PLAN

SCALE: 0 16 32 48 64 FEET

SENATE WING

MEZZANINE

HOUSE WING

MEZZANINE

COURT

COURT

SUB-BASEMENT

SUBWAY TERMINAL

SUBWAY TERMINAL
(UNDER CONSTRUCTION)

FIRST FLOOR PLAN

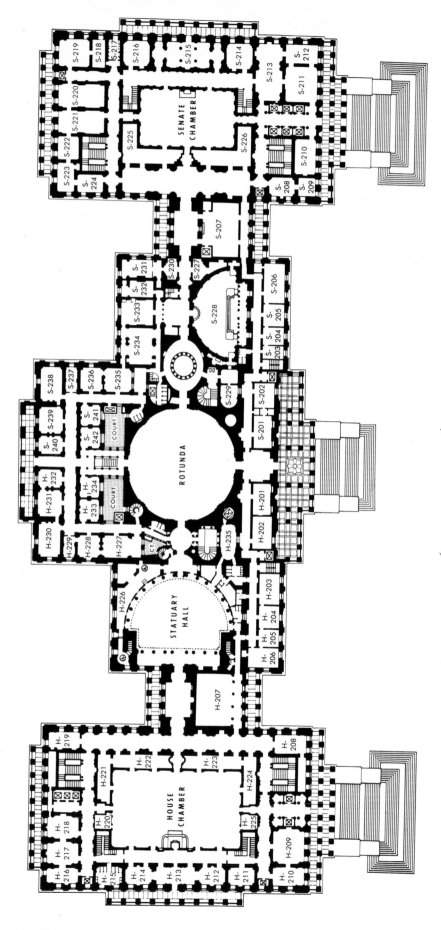

SECOND (PRINCIPAL) FLOOR PLAN

SCALE: 0   16   32   48   64   FEET

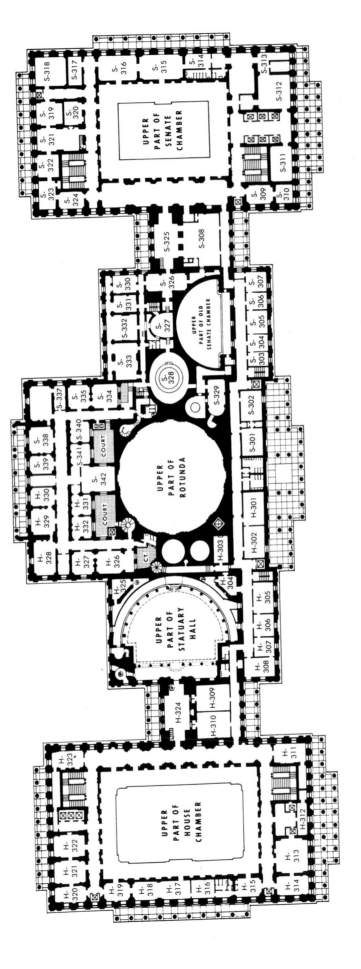

THIRD (GALLERY) FLOOR PLAN

SCALE: 0 16 32 48 64 FEET

UPPER PART OF SENATE CHAMBER

S-318 S-317 S-316 S-315 S-314 S-313 S-312
S-319 S-320 S-311
S-321 S-322 S-309 S-310
S-323 S-324

S-325 S-308

UPPER PART OF OLD SENATE CHAMBER

S-330 S-331 S-326 S-307 S-306
S-332 S-327 S-305 S-304
S-333 S-303
S-328 S-329 S-302
S-337 S-335 S-334 S-301

UPPER PART OF ROTUNDA

S-338 S-340 COURT
S-339 S-341
330 S-342
H-329 H-331 H-301
H-328 H-332 COURT H-302
H-327 H-303
H-326 H-304
H-325 H-305
H-324 H-306 H-307

UPPER PART OF STATUARY HALL

H-310 H-309 H-308

UPPER PART OF HOUSE CHAMBER

H-323 H-311
H-322 H-312
H-321 H-313
H-320 H-314
H-319 H-318 H-317 H-316 H-315

Statues in the United States Capitol Contributed by States to the National Statuary Hall Collection

NATIONAL STATUARY HALL—LEGISLATION AND HISTORY

The history of National Statuary Hall in the United States Capitol dates back to the middle of the nineteenth century. The former Chamber had been vacant for seven years after housing the House of Representatives for a half century (1807–1857) when the new South wing of the Capitol was completed and the House moved into its new Chamber.

As early as 1853, however, Gouverneur Kemble, formerly a member of the House of Representatives, had written to Montgomery C. Meigs, in charge of the construction of the Dome and Senate and House wings, of his suggestions for the use of the Hall. In 1854 he came to the Capitol and discussed the prospect of exhibiting historical paintings. It was finally decided that the space between the columns was too limited for such a purpose. The suggestion was then made that the Hall be used for the display of busts and statues of distinguished Americans.

On April 19, 1864, the Honorable Justin S. Morrill in the House of Representatives proposed, "To what end more useful or grand, and at the same time simple and inexpensive, can we devote it [the Chamber] than to ordain that it shall be set apart for the reception of such statuary as each State shall elect to be deserving of this lasting commemoration?" His proposal was enacted into the law creating the National Statuary Hall.

The law creating Statuary Hall, and designating the action to be taken in connection with the presentation of statues, is known as the act of July 2, 1864 (sec. 1814 of the Revised Statutes), the essential portion of which provides:

Suitable structures and railings shall be erected in the Old Hall of Representatives for the reception and protection of statuary * * *

And the President is hereby authorized to invite each and all the States to provide and furnish statues, in marble or bronze, not exceeding two in number for each State, of deceased persons who have been citizens thereof, and illustrious for their historic renown or for distinguished civic or military services such as each State may deem to be worthy of this national commemoration; and when so furnished the same shall be placed in the Old Hall of the House of Representatives, in the Capitol of the United States, which is set apart, or so much thereof as may be necessary, as a national statuary hall for the purpose herein indicated.

Due to structural conditions in Statuary Hall, Congress, on February 24, 1933, passed House Concurrent Resolution No. 47 to provide for the relocation of statues and also to govern the future reception and location of statues, which reads as follows:

Resolved by the House of Representatives (the Senate concurring), That the Architect of the Capitol, upon the approval of the Joint Committee on the Library, with the advice of the Commission of Fine Arts, is hereby authorized and directed to relocate within the Capitol any of the statues already received and placed in Statuary Hall, and to provide for the reception and location of the statues received hereafter from the States.

Under authority of this resolution, it was decided that hereafter not to exceed one statue from each State shall be placed in Statuary Hall; the others to be located elsewhere in the building.

Eighty-six statues (45 marble and 41 bronze) have been contributed to date by 47 States to the National Statuary Hall, under authority of the act of July 2, 1864 (sec. 1814 of the Revised Statutes), as amended by House Concurrent Resolution

47, Seventy-second Congress, authorizing the States to contribute 2 statues each.

Two statues have been received from each of the following 39 States: Alabama, Arkansas, California, Connecticut, Delaware, Florida, Georgia, Idaho, Illinois, Indiana, Iowa, Kansas, Kentucky, Louisiana, Maine, Maryland, Massachusetts, Michigan, Minnesota, Mississippi, Missouri, Nebraska, New Hampshire, New Jersey, New York, North Carolina, Ohio, Oklahoma, Oregon, Pennsylvania, Rhode Island, South Carolina, South Dakota, Tennessee, Texas, Vermont, Virginia, West Virginia, and Wisconsin.

One statue has been received from each of the following 8 States: Arizona, Colorado, Montana, Nevada, North Dakota, Utah, Washington, and Wyoming.

No statues have been received from the following 3 States: Alaska, Hawaii, New Mexico.

A statue of Eusebio Francisco Kino, the second statue from Arizona, is now nearing completion and is scheduled for delivery early in 1965.

LIST OF STATUES BY STATES CONTRIBUTED TO THE NATIONAL STATUARY HALL COLLECTION

STATE	NAME OF STATUE	NAME OF SCULPTOR
Alabama	Jabez Lamar Monroe Curry General Joseph Wheeler	Dante Sodini Berthold Nebel
Alaska		
Arizona	John Campbell Greenway Eusebio F. Kino (nearing completion)	Gutzon Borglum
Arkansas	Uriah M. Rose James Paul Clarke	Frederic Wellington Ruckstull Pompeo Coppini
California	Thomas Starr King Junipero Serra	Haig Patigian Ettore Cadorin
Colorado	Dr. Florence Rena Sabin	Joy Buba
Connecticut	Roger Sherman Jonathan Trumbull	Chauncey B. Ives Chauncey B. Ives
Delaware	Caesar Rodney John Middleton Clayton	Bryant Baker Bryant Baker
Florida	Dr. John Gorrie Gen. Edmund Kirby Smith	Charles Adrian Pillars Charles Adrian Pillars
Georgia	Dr. Crawford W. Long Alexander H. Stephens	J. Massey Rhind Gutzon Borglum
Hawaii		
Idaho	George L. Shoup William Edgar Borah	Frederick Ernst Triebel Bryant Baker

STATE	NAME OF STATUE	NAME OF SCULPTOR
Illinois...............	General James Shields	Leonard Wells Volk
	Frances E. Willard	Helen Farnsworth Mears
Indiana...............	Oliver Hazard Perry (Throck) Morton	Charles Henry Niehaus
	General Lew Wallace	Andrew O'Connor
Iowa................	James Harlan	Nellie V. Walker
	Samuel Jordan Kirkwood	Vinnie Ream Hoxie
Kansas..............	John James Ingalls	Charles Henry Niehaus
	George Washington Glick	Charles Henry Niehaus
Kentucky.............	Henry Clay	Charles Henry Niehaus
	Dr. Ephraim McDowell	Charles Henry Niehaus
Louisiana.............	Huey Pierce Long	Charles Keck
	Edward Douglass White	Arthur C. Morgan
Maine................	William King	Franklin Simmons
	Hannibal Hamlin	Charles E. Tefft
Maryland.............	Charles Carroll of Carrollton	Richard E. Brooks
	John Hanson	Richard E. Brooks
Massachusetts..........	Samuel Adams	Anne Whitney
	John Winthrop	Richard S. Greenough
Michigan.............	Lewis Cass	Daniel Chester French
	Zachariah Chandler	Charles Henry Niehaus
Minnesota............	Henry Mower Rice	Frederick Ernst Triebel
	Maria L. Sanford	Evelyn Raymond
Mississippi...........	Jefferson Davis	Augustus Lukeman
	James Zachariah George	Augustus Lukeman
Missouri..............	Francis P. Blair, Jr.	Alexander Doyle
	Thomas Hart Benton	Alexander Doyle
Montana.............	Charles Marion Russell	John B. Weaver
	....	....
Nebraska.............	William Jennings Bryan	Rudolph Evans
	J. Sterling Morton	Rudolph Evans
Nevada..............	Patrick Anthony McCarran	Yolande Jacobson (Mrs. J. Craig Sheppard)
	....	....
New Hampshire........	John Stark (replica)	Carl Conrads
	Daniel Webster (after the original by Thomas Ball)	Carl Conrads
New Jersey............	Richard Stockton	Henry Kirke Brown (completed by H. K. Bush-Brown)
	Philip Kearny	Henry Kirke Brown

STATE	NAME OF STATUE	NAME OF SCULPTOR
New Mexico...........	....	....
	....	....
New York.............	Robert Livingston	Erastus Dow Palmer
	George Clinton	Henry Kirke Brown
North Carolina.........	Zebulon Baird Vance	Gutzon Borglum
	Charles Brantley Aycock	Charles Keck
North Dakota..........	John Burke	Avard Fairbanks
	....	....
Ohio................	James Garfield	Charles Henry Niehaus
	William Allen	Charles Henry Niehaus
Oklahoma............	Sequoyah (Sequoya)	Vinnie Ream Hoxie (completed by George Julian Zolnay)
	Will Rogers	Jo Davidson
Oregon..............	Reverend Jason Lee	G. MacG. Proctor
	John McLoughlin	Gifford Proctor
Pennsylvania..........	John Peter Gabriel Muhlenberg	Blanche Nevin
	Robert Fulton	Howard Roberts
Rhode Island..........	Nathanael Greene	Henry Kirke Brown
	Roger Williams	Franklin Simmons
South Carolina.........	John C. Calhoun	Frederic Wellington Ruckstull
	Wade Hampton	Frederic Wellington Ruckstull
South Dakota.........	William H. H. Beadle (replica)	H. Daniel Webster
	Joseph Ward	Bruno Beghe
Tennessee.............	Andrew Jackson	Belle Kinney Scholz and Leopold F. Scholz
	John Sevier	Belle Kinney Scholz and Leopold F. Scholz
Texas...............	Stephen F. Austin	Elisabet Ney
	Samuel Houston	Elisabet Ney
Utah................	Brigham Young	Mahonri Young
	....	....
Vermont..............	Ethan Allen	Larkin G. Mead
	Jacob Collamer	Preston Powers
Virginia.............	Robert E. Lee	Edward V. Valentine
	George Washington	William Hubard (after the original by Antoine Houdon)

STATE	NAME OF STATUE	NAME OF SCULPTOR
Washington...........	Marcus Whitman	Avard Fairbanks
	....	....
West Virginia.........	John E. Kenna	Alexander Doyle
	Francis H. Pierpont	Franklin Simmons
Wisconsin............	Pere Jacques (James) Marquette	Gaetano Trentanove
	Robert Marion La Follette, Sr.	Jo Davidson
Wyoming.............	Esther Hobart Morris	Avard Fairbanks
	....	....

Locations in the Capitol Building of Statues Contributed by States

(List of 47 Statues in Statuary Hall—1 Statue from Each State Contributing)*

STATE	NAME OF STATUE	NAME OF SCULPTOR
Alabama.............	Gen. Joe Wheeler	Berthold Nebel
Arkansas.............	Uriah M. Rose	F. W. Ruckstull
Arizona.............	John Campbell Greenway	Gutzon Borglum
California............	Junipero Serra	Ettore Cadorin
Colorado............	Dr. Florence Rena Sabin	Joy Buba
Connecticut...........	Roger Sherman	Chauncey B. Ives
Delaware.............	Caesar Rodney	Bryant Baker
Florida.............	John Gorrie	C. A. Pillars
Georgia.............	Alexander H. Stephens	Gutzon Borglum
Idaho...............	George L. Shoup	F. E. Triebel
Illinois.............	Frances E. Willard	Helen Farnsworth Mears
Indiana.............	Gen. Lew Wallace	Andrew O'Connor
Iowa...............	S. J. Kirkwood	Vinnie Ream Hoxie
Kansas.............	John J. Ingalls	C. H. Niehaus
Kentucky............	Henry Clay	C. H. Niehaus
Louisiana............	Huey P. Long	Charles Keck
Maine...............	Hannibal Hamlin	Charles E. Tefft
Maryland.............	Charles Carroll	R. E. Brooks
Massachusetts..........	Samuel Adams	Anne Whitney
Michigan.............	Lewis Cass	D. C. French
Minnesota............	Henry M. Rice	F. E. Triebel
Mississippi...........	Jefferson Davis	Augustus Lukeman
Missouri.............	Thomas H. Benton	Alexander Doyle
Montana.............	Charles Marion Russell	John B. Weaver
Nebraska.............	William Jennings Bryan	Rudulph Evans
Nevada.............	Patrick A. McCarran	Yolande Jacobson (Mrs. J. Craig Sheppard)

* Marble—24 statues; Bronze—23 statues; 11 statues were placed in Statuary Hall since 1934 relocation: Rodney, Huey Long, Hamlin, Bryan, Beadle, Burke, Russell, McCarran, Jason Lee, Whitman, Morris.

STATE	NAME OF STATUE	NAME OF SCULPTOR
New Hampshire.........	Daniel Webster	Carl Conrads
New Jersey.............	Richard Stockton	H. K. Brown
New York..............	Robert R. Livingston	Erastus Dow Palmer
North Carolina........	Zebulon B. Vance	Gutzon Borglum
North Dakota.........	John Burke	Avard Fairbanks
Ohio..................	William Allen	C. H. Niehaus
Oklahoma.............	Sequoyah (Sequoya)[1]	Vinnie Ream Hoxie
Oregon...............	Rev. Jason Lee	G. MacG. Proctor
Pennsylvania..........	Robert Fulton	Howard Roberts
Rhode Island..........	Roger Williams	Franklin Simmons
South Carolina........	John C. Calhoun	F. W. Ruckstull
South Dakota..........	Gen. William Henry H. Beadle	H. Daniel Webster
Tennessee.............	John Sevier	Belle K. and L. F. Scholz
Texas.................	Samuel Houston	Elisabet Ney
Utah.................	Brigham Young	Mahronri Young
Vermont..............	Ethan Allen	Larkin G. Mead
Virginia..............	Robert E. Lee	Edward V. Valentine
Washington...........	Marcus Whitman	Avard Fairbanks
West Virginia..........	Francis H. Pierpont	Franklin Simmons
Wisconsin	Robert M. La Follette, Sr.	Jo Davidson
Wyoming..............	Esther H. Morris	Avard Fairbanks

[1] In addition to his native name, Sequoya was also known as George Gist, often spelled Guest or Guess.

3 Statues Located in the Rotunda—(Relocated from Statuary Hall)

Ohio.................	James A. Garfield	C. H. Niehaus
Tennessee.............	Andrew Jackson	Belle Kinney Scholz, and L. F. Scholz
Virginia..............	George Washington	William Hubard (after Houdon)

3 Statues Located in Vestibule South of Rotunda—(Relocated from Statuary Hall)

New York.............	George Clinton	H. K. Brown
Pennsylvania...........	J. P. G. Muhlenberg	Blanche Nevin
Texas.................	Stephen F. Austin	Elisabet Ney

2 Statues Located in Vestibule of Former Supreme Court Room—(Relocated from Statuary Hall)

New Hampshire.........	John Stark	Carl Conrads
Rhode Island..........	Gen. Nathanael Greene	H. K. Brown

7 Statues Located in Senate Connection—(Relocated from Statuary Hall, Except Statues of John M. Clayton, William E. Borah, Maria L. Sanford, and Edward D. White)

STATE	NAME OF STATUE	NAME OF SCULPTOR
Delaware	John M. Clayton	Bryant Baker
Georgia	Dr. Crawford W. Long	J. Massey Rhind
Idaho	William E. Borah	Bryant Baker
Kentucky	Dr. Ephraim McDowell	C. H. Niehaus
Louisiana	Edward D. White	Arthur C. Morgan
Maryland	John Hanson	R. E. Brooks
Minnesota	Maria L. Sanford	Evelyn Raymond

6 Statues Located in House Connection—(Relocated from Statuary Hall, Except Statues of Will Rogers and Dr. John McLoughlin)

Wisconsin	Pere Jaques (James) Marquette	G. Trentanove
Connecticut	Jonathan Trumbull	C. B. Ives
Maine	William King	Franklin Simmons
Oregon	Dr. John McLoughlin	Gifford Proctor
South Carolina	Wade Hampton	F. W. Ruckstull
Oklahoma	Will Rogers	Jo Davidson

18 Statues Located in the Hall of Columns—(All Relocated from Statuary Hall, Except Statues of J. Sterling Morton and Joseph Ward)

Alabama	J. L. M. Curry	Dante Sodini
Arkansas	James P. Clarke	Pompeo Coppini
California	Thomas Starr King	Haig Patigian
Florida	Gen. E. Kirby Smith	C. A. Pillars
Illinois	Gen. James Shields	L. W. Volk
Indiana	Oliver P. Morton	C. H. Niehaus
Iowa	James Harlan	Nellie V. Walker
Kansas	George W. Glick	C. H. Niehaus
Massachusetts	John Winthrop	R. S. Greenough
Michigan	Zachariah Chandler	C. H. Niehaus
Mississippi	James Z. George	Augustus Lukeman
Missouri	Francis P. Blair, Jr.	Alexander Doyle
Nebraska	J. Sterling Morton	Rudulph Evans
New Jersey	Gen. Philip Kearny	H. K. Brown
North Carolina	Charles Brantley Aycock	Charles Keck
South Dakota	Joseph Ward	Bruno Beghe
Vermont	Jacob Collamer	Preston Powers
West Virginia	John E. Kenna	Alexander Doyle

STATUE	STATE	SCULPTOR	MARBLE OR BRONZE	UNVEILING, ACCEPTANCE OR PROCEEDINGS IN CONGRESS	LOCATION
Adams, Samuel...........	Massachusetts	Anne Whitney	Marble	Congressional Proceedings (1876)	Statuary Hall
Allen, Ethan.............	Vermont	Larkin G. Mead	Marble	Congressional Proceedings (1876)	Statuary Hall
Allen, William...........	Ohio	Charles H. Niehaus	Marble	Placed (1887)	Statuary Hall
Austin, Stephen F.........	Texas	Elisabet Ney	Marble	Congressional Proceedings (1905)	Vestibule south of Rotunda
Aycock, Charles Brantley...	North Carolina	Charles Keck	Bronze	Unveiled (1932)	Hall of Columns
Beadle, William H. H......	South Dakota	H. Daniel Webster	Bronze	Unveiled (1938)	Statuary Hall
Benton, Thomas H........	Missouri	Alexander Doyle	Marble	Congressional Proceedings (1899)	Statuary Hall
Blair, Francis P., Jr.......	Missouri	Alexander Doyle	Marble	Congressional Proceedings (1899)	Hall of Columns
Borah, William E.........	Idaho	Bryant Baker	Bronze	Unveiled (1947)	Senate connection
Bryan, William Jennings....	Nebraska	Rudulph Evans	Bronze	Unveiled (1937)	Statuary Hall
Burke, John..............	North Dakota	Avard Fairbanks	Bronze	Unveiled (1963)	Statuary Hall
Calhoun, John C..........	South Carolina	Frederic W. Ruckstull	Marble	Unveiled (1910)	Statuary Hall
Carroll, Charles, of Carrollton	Maryland	Richard E. Brooks	Bronze	Congressional Proceedings (1903)	Statuary Hall
Cass, Lewis..............	Michigan	Daniel Chester French	Marble	Congressional Proceedings (1889)	Statuary Hall
Chandler, Zachariah.......	Michigan........	Charles H. Niehaus	Marble	Unveiled (1913)	Hall of Columns
Clarke, James P...........	Arkansas	Pompeo Coppini	Marble	Placed (1921)	Hall of Columns
Clay, Henry..............	Kentucky	Charles H. Niehaus	Bronze	Unveiled (1929)	Statuary Hall
Clayton, John M..........	Delaware	Bryant Baker	Marble	Unveiled (1934)	Senate connection
Clinton, George..........	New York	Henry Kirke Brown	Bronze	Placed (1873)	Vestibule south of Rotunda
Collamer, Jacob...........	Vermont	Preston Powers	Marble	Congressional Proceedings (1881)	Hall of Columns
Curry, Jabez Lamar Monroe.	Alabama	Dante Sodini	Marble	Congressional Proceedings (1908)	Hall of Columns
Davis, Jefferson...........	Mississippi	Augustus Lukeman	Bronze	Unveiled (1931)	Statuary Hall
Fulton, Robert............	Pennsylvania	Howard Roberts	Marble	Congressional Proceedings (1889)	Statuary Hall
Garfield, James A.........	Ohio	Charles H. Niehaus	Marble	Congressional Proceedings (1886)	Rotunda
George, James Z..........	Mississippi	Augustus Lukeman	Bronze	Unveiled (1931)	Hall of Columns
Glick, George W..........	Kansas	Charles H. Niehaus	Marble	Congressional Proceedings (1914)	Hall of Columns
Gorrie, John.............	Florida	C. A. Pillars	Marble	Unveiled (1914)	Statuary Hall
Greene, Nathanael.........	Rhode Island	Henry Kirke Brown	Marble	Congressional Proceedings (1870)	Vestibule of Old Supreme Court Chamber
Greenway, John C.........	Arizona	Gutzon Borglum	Bronze	Unveiled (1930)	Statuary Hall
Hamlin, Hannibal.........	Maine	Charles E. Tefft	Bronze	Unveiled (1935)	Statuary Hall
Hampton, Wade..........	South Carolina	Frederic W. Ruckstull	Marble	Unveiled (1929)	House connection
Hanson, John.............	Maryland	Richard E. Brooks	Bronze	Congressional Proceedings (1903)	Senate connection

STATUE	STATE	SCULPTOR	MARBLE OR BRONZE	UNVEILING, ACCEPTANCE OR PROCEEDINGS IN CONGRESS	LOCATION
Harlan, James............	Iowa	Nellie V. Walker	Bronze	Installed (1910)	Hall of Columns
Houston, Samuel..........	Texas	Elisabet Ney	Marble	Congressional Proceedings (1905)	Statuary Hall
Ingalls, John J............	Kansas	Charles H. Niehaus	Marble	Congressional Proceedings (1905)	Statuary Hall
Jackson, Andrew..........	Tennessee	Belle Kinney Scholz and Leopold F. Scholz	Bronze	Unveiled (1928)	Rotunda
Kearny, Philip.............	New Jersey	Henry Kirke Brown	Bronze	Congressional Proceedings (1888)	Hall of Columns
Kenna, John E.............	West Virginia	Alexander Doyle	Marble	Placed 1901	Hall of Columns
King, Thomas Starr.......	California	Haig Patigian	Bronze	Unveiled (1931)	Hall of Columns
King, William............	Maine	Franklin Simmons	Marble	Congressional Proceedings (1878)	House connection
Kirkwood, Samuel J.......	Iowa	Vinnie Ream Hoxie	Bronze	Placed (1913)	Statuary Hall
La Follette, Robert M., Sr..	Wisconsin	Jo Davidson	Marble	Unveiled (1929)	Statuary Hall
Lee, Rev. Jason...........	Oregon	G. MacG. Proctor [1]	Bronze	Unveiled (1953)	Statuary Hall
Lee, Robert E............	Virginia	Edward V. Valentine	Bronze	Unveiled (1934)	Statuary Hall
Livingston, Robert R.......	New York	Erastus Dow Palmer	Bronze	Placed (1875)	Statuary Hall
Long, Dr. Crawford W.....	Georgia	J. Massey Rhind	Marble	Unveiled (1926)	Senate connection
Long, Huey P.............	Louisiana	Charles Keck	Bronze	Unveiled (1941)	Statuary Hall
Marquette, (Pere Jacques) James	Wisconsin	Gaetano Trentanove	Marble	Congressional Proceedings (1896)	House connection
McCarran, Patrick A.......	Nevada	Yolande Jacobson (Mrs. J. Craig Sheppard)	Bronze	Unveiled (1960)	Statuary Hall Vestibule— North
McDowell, Dr. Ephraim...	Kentucky	Charles H. Niehaus	Bronze	Unveiled (1929)	Senate connection
McLoughlin, Dr. John......	Oregon	Gifford Proctor [1]	Bronze	Unveiled (1953)	House connection
Morris, Esther H..........	Wyoming	Avard Fairbanks	Bronze	Unveiled (1960)	Statuary Hall Vestibule— North
Morton, J. Sterling........	Nebraska	Rudulph Evans	Bronze	Unveiled (1937)	Hall of Columns
Morton, Oliver P..........	Indiana	Charles H. Niehaus	Marble	Congressional Proceedings (1900)	Hall of Columns
Muhlenberg, John P. G.....	Pennsylvania	Blanche Nevin	Marble	Congressional Proceedings (1889)	Vestibule south of Rotunda
Pierpont, Francis H........	West Virginia	Franklin Simmons	Marble	Unveiled (1910)	Statuary Hall
Rice, Henry Mower........	Minnesota	Frederick E. Triebel	Marble	Unveiled (1916)	Statuary Hall
Rodney, Caesar............	Delaware	Bryant Baker	Marble	Unveiled (1934)	Statuary Hall
Rogers, Will..............	Oklahoma	Jo Davidson	Bronze	Unveiled (1939)	House connection
Rose, Uriah M............	Arkansas	Frederic W. Ruckstull	Marble	Placed (1917)	Statuary Hall
Russell, Charles M.........	Montana	John B. Weaver	Bronze	Unveiled (1959)	Statuary Hall
Sabin, Dr. Florence R......	Colorado	Joy Buba	Bronze	Unveiled (1959)	Statuary Hall
Sanford, Maria L..........	Minnesota	Evelyn Raymond	Bronze	Unveiled (1958)	Senate connection
Sequoyah (Sequoya).......	Oklahoma	Vinnie Ream Hoxie (completed by G. Julian Zolnay)	Bronze	Unveiled (1917)	Statuary Hall

[1] Joint commission for the Oregon statues was given to A. Phimister Proctor and his son, Gifford. A. Phimister Proctor died before the models were completed. The statues were completed by Gifford (G. MacG.) Proctor.

211

STATUE	STATE	SCULPTOR	MARBLE OR BRONZE	UNVEILING, ACCEPTANCE OR PROCEEDINGS IN CONGRESS	LOCATION
Serra, Junipero............	California	Ettore Cadorin	Bronze	Unveiled (1931)	Statuary Hall
Sevier, John..............	Tennessee	Belle Kinney Scholz and Leopold F. Scholz	Bronze	Unveiled (1931)	Statuary Hall
Sherman, Roger...........	Connecticut	Chauncey B. Ives	Marble	Congressional Proceedings (1872)	Statuary Hall
Shields, Gen. James......	Illinois	Leonard W. Volk	Bronze	Unveiled (1893)	Hall of Columns
Shoup, George L..........	Idaho	Frederick E. Triebel	Marble	Congressional Proceedings (1910)	Statuary Hall
Smith, Gen. E. Kirby......	Florida	C. Adrian Pillars	Bronze	Congressional Proceedings (1922)	Hall of Columns
Stark, John (Replica)......	New Hampshire	Carl Conrads	Marble	Congressional Proceedings (1894)	Vestibule of Old Supreme Court Chamber
Stephens, Alexander H.....	Georgia	Gutzon Borglum	Marble	Unveiled (1927)	Statuary Hall
Stockton, Richard.........	New Jersey	Henry Kirke Brown (completed by H. K. Bush-Brown)	Marble	Congressional Proceedings (1888)	Statuary Hall
Trumbull, Jonathan........	Connecticut	Chauncey B. Ives	Marble	Congressional Proceedings (1871)	House connection
Vance, Zebulon Baird......	North Carolina	Gutzon Borglum	Bronze	Unveiled (1916)	Statuary Hall
Wallace, General Lew......	Indiana	Andrew O'Connor	Marble	Unveiled (1910)	Statuary Hall
Ward, Joseph..............	South Dakota	Bruno Beghe	Marble	Unveiled (1963)	Hall of Columns
Washington, George.......	Virginia	William Hubard (after Houdon)	Bronze	Unveiled (1934)	Rotunda
Webster, Daniel........... (After original by Thomas Ball).	New Hampshire	Carl Conrads	Marble	Congressional Proceedings (1894)	Statuary Hall
Wheeler, General Joseph....	Alabama	Berthold Nebel	Bronze	Unveiled (1925)	Statuary Hall
White, Edward Douglass...	Louisiana	Arthur C. Morgan	Bronze	Unveiled (1955)	Senate connection
Whitman, Marcus..........	Washington	Avard Fairbanks	Bronze	Unveiled (1953)	Statuary Hall
Willard, Frances E.........	Illinois	Helen Farnsworth Mears	Marble	Congressional Proceedings (1905)	Statuary Hall
Williams, Roger...........	Rhode Island	Franklin Simmons	Marble	Congressional Proceedings (1872)	Statuary Hall
Winthrop, John............	Massachusetts	Richard S. Greenough	Marble	Congressional Proceedings (1876)	Hall of Columns
Young, Brigham...........	Utah	Mahonri Young	Marble	Unveiled (1950)	Statuary Hall

212

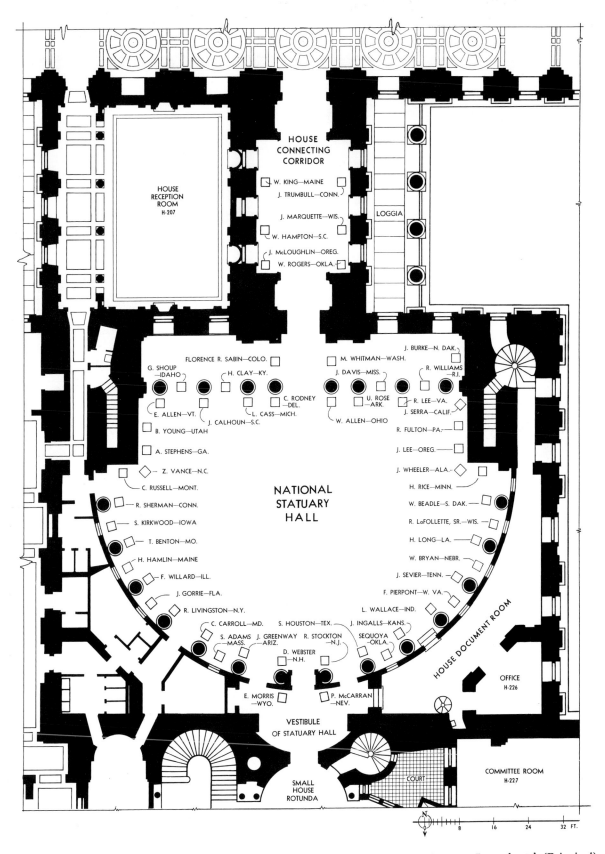

HOUSE CONNECTING CORRIDOR

W. KING—MAINE
J. TRUMBULL—CONN.

J. MARQUETTE—WIS.
W. HAMPTON—S.C.

J. McLOUGHLIN—OREG.
W. ROGERS—OKLA.

HOUSE RECEPTION ROOM H-207

LOGGIA

NATIONAL STATUARY HALL

FLORENCE R. SABIN—COLO.
G. SHOUP —IDAHO
H. CLAY—KY.
C. RODNEY —DEL.
E. ALLEN—VT.
J. CALHOUN—S.C.
L. CASS—MICH.
B. YOUNG—UTAH
A. STEPHENS—GA.
Z. VANCE—N.C.
C. RUSSELL—MONT.
R. SHERMAN—CONN.
S. KIRKWOOD—IOWA
T. BENTON—MO.
H. HAMLIN—MAINE
F. WILLARD—ILL.
J. GORRIE—FLA.
R. LIVINGSTON—N.Y.
C. CARROLL—MD.
S. ADAMS —MASS.
J. GREENWAY —ARIZ.
D. WEBSTER —N.H.
R. STOCKTON —N.J.
E. MORRIS —WYO.
P. McCARRAN —NEV.

M. WHITMAN—WASH.
J. DAVIS—MISS.
J. BURKE—N. DAK.
R. WILLIAMS —R.I.
U. ROSE —ARK.
R. LEE—VA.
J. SERRA—CALIF.
W. ALLEN—OHIO
R. FULTON—PA.
J. LEE—OREG.
J. WHEELER—ALA.
H. RICE—MINN.
W. BEADLE—S. DAK.
R. LaFOLLETTE, SR.—WIS.
H. LONG—LA.
W. BRYAN—NEBR.
J. SEVIER—TENN.
F. PIERPONT—W. VA.
L. WALLACE—IND.
J. INGALLS—KANS.
S. HOUSTON—TEX.
SEQUOYA —OKLA.

HOUSE DOCUMENT ROOM

OFFICE H-226

VESTIBULE OF STATUARY HALL

SMALL HOUSE ROTUNDA

COURT

COMMITTEE ROOM H-227

N

8   16   24   32 FT.

Plan of Statuary Hall, Adjacent Vestibule, House Connecting Corridor and small House Rotunda, 2d (Principal) Floor, House Wing, Showing Location of Statues.

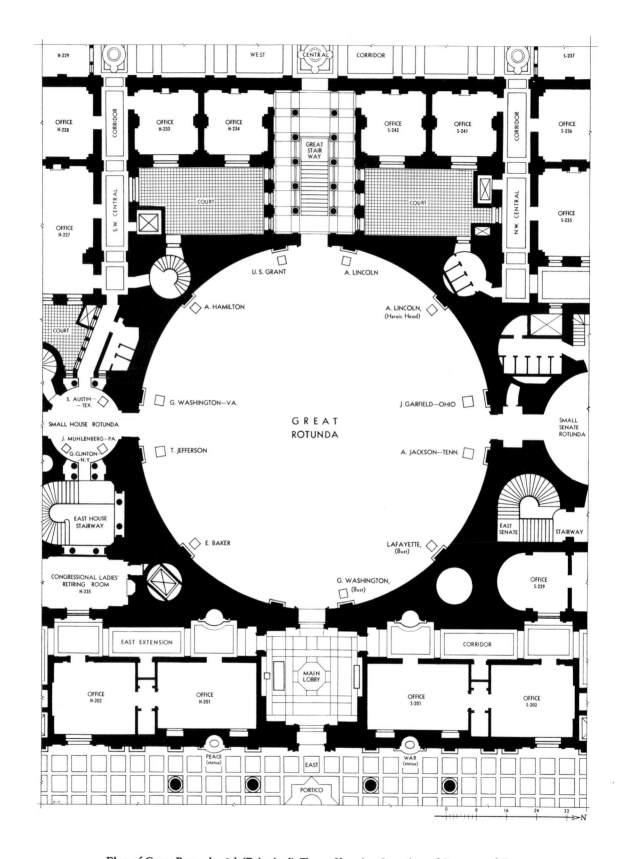

Plan of Great Rotunda, 2d (Principal) Floor, Showing Location of Statues and Busts.

214

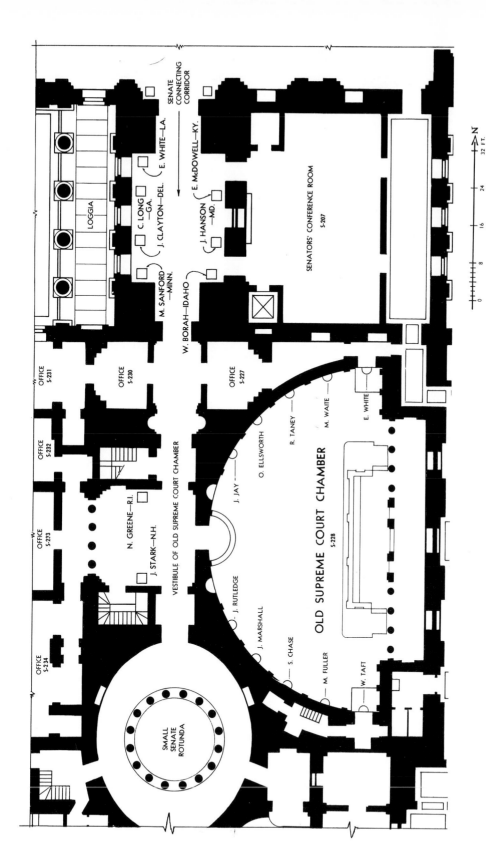

Plan of Old Supreme Court Section, 2d (Principal) Floor, Showing Location of Busts in Old Supreme Court Chamber, Statues in Adjacent Vestibule and Senate Connecting Corridor.

215

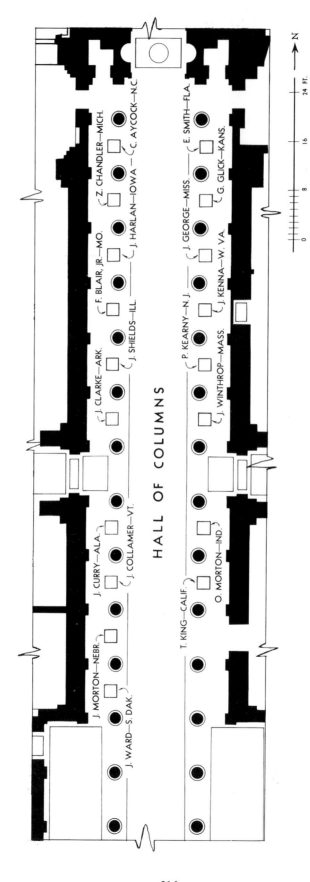

Plan of Hall of Columns, 1st (Ground) Floor, House Wing, Showing the Location of a Part of the Statues From Statuary Hall Collection.

BIOGRAPHIES OF CITIZENS COMMEMORATED BY STATUES FROM STATES

Eighty-six citizens "illustrious for their historic renown or distinguished civic or military service" as required under section 1814 of the Revised Statutes of the United States, having been selected by the States for commemoration, their brief biographies follow:

Alabama—J. L. M. Curry (1825–1903) and General Joseph Wheeler (1836–1906).

J. L. M. Curry was a soldier, statesman, educator and orator; served in the War with Mexico and the Civil War; Member of the U.S. House of Representatives, 1857–61; resigned to become a Member of the Confederate Congress, 1861–64; professor and college president; Minister to Spain.

Gen. Wheeler, a graduate of West Point, served in the Confederate Army and attained the rank of senior cavalry officer; he also served in the United States Army during the War with Spain and was made brigadier general; his services as a Representative in Congress included service in the Forty-seventh, Forty-ninth, and the seven following Congresses.

Arizona—John Campbell Greenway (1872–1926).

Gen. Greenway was distinguished as a soldier in the War with Spain, and World War I. During the War with Spain he was a member of the celebrated cavalry organization known as the Rough Riders. His service in the World War was one of distinction. He was commissioned Brigadier General in 1922. In private life he was a noted mining engineer and inventor of the turbo log washer.

Arkansas—Uriah M. Rose (1834–1913) and James P. Clarke (1854–1916).

Uriah M. Rose was a lawyer of international reputation; chancellor of the State; charter member of American Bar Association, serving as president in 1901. He authored the "Arkansas Constitution" and "Digest of Arkansas Reports." In 1907 he was appointed by President Roosevelt as one of the delegates to the Peace Congress of The

Hague and was given the rank of ambassador upon that mission.

James P. Clarke was a lawyer, State attorney general, Governor of Arkansas, and United States Senator from March 4, 1903, until the time of his death, October 1, 1916; served as President pro tempore of the Senate 1913–1916.

California—Junipero Serra (1713–84) and Thomas Starr King (1824–64).

Father Junipero Serra was a missionary of the Franciscan Order. When Franciscans were sent to lower California, Serra went as their president. He established nine missions, those venerable temples which are California's best titles to fame.

Thomas Starr King, preacher, patriot, orator; ordained as a minister when 22 years old; received a call in 1860 to the First Unitarian Church of California. During his 4 years service in San Francisco he was a dominant factor in the support of the Union. His portrait hangs in the capitol at Sacramento; it bears this inscription:

"The man whose matchless oratory saved California to the Union."

Colorado—Dr. Florence Rena Sabin (1871–1953)

Dr. Florence R. Sabin was distinguished as a teacher, scientist, humanitarian and writer of medical texts; as a woman she pioneered membership into the National Academy of Sciences, entrance into Johns Hopkins Medical School; faculty member of the Rockefeller Institute of Medical Research; she was instrumental in the drafting and enacting of the "Sabin Health Laws" in Colorado.

Connecticut—Roger Sherman (1721–93) and Jonathan Trumbull (1710–85).

Roger Sherman was the only member of the Continental Congress to affix his signature to all four of the great State papers relating to the founding of this Nation—the Declaration of 1774, the Declaration of Independence, the Articles of Confederation, and the Federal Constitution. He served in the Connecticut legislature, the Continental Congress, the Constitutional Convention, the U.S. House of Representatives, 1789–91, and the U.S. Senate, 1791–93.

Jonathan Trumbull was a soldier, statesman and minister who espoused the cause of independence, aided General Washington, and worked for a stronger Union. In his early years he was one of the outstanding figures of Connecticut commerce, later devoting his life to politics. He served in the Connecticut Assembly, held the Governorship for 15 years, and served as the State's chief justice in colonial times, 1769–1784. He was the father of the artist John Trumbull, painter of four of the paintings in the Rotunda, United States Capitol.

Delaware—Caesar Rodney (1728–84) and John M. Clayton (1796–1856).

Caesar Rodney was a delegate to the Stamp Act Congress, signer of the Declaration of Independence, a Member of the Continental Congress, Major General in the Revolutionary War; was in command at the Battle of Trenton; President of Delaware, 1778–1782; and occupied many positions of note in his native State.

John M. Clayton was noted as a jurist, a statesman and a diplomat. He served his State as a member of the house of representatives, secretary of state and chief justice; Member of the U.S. Senate, 1829–36, elected again to U.S. Senate, served from 1845 to 1849, when he resigned to accept position of Secretary of State under President Taylor; negotiated the Clayton-Bulwer Treaty and again elected to the U.S. Senate and served from 1853 until his death.

Florida—Dr. John Gorrie (1803–55) and General Edmund Kirby Smith (1824–93).

Dr. Gorrie was an eminent physician and held the first patent on mechanical refrigeration which he developed to alleviate the suffering of the sick. This later led to discoveries of air conditioning and mechanical ice-making.

General Smith was a graduate with honors of West Point, soldier in the War with Mexico and General in the Confederate Army. He served as Chancellor of the University of Nashville (Tennessee), and taught mathematics at West Point, 1849–52, and the University of Sewanee (Tennessee).

Georgia—Dr. Crawford Williamson Long (1815–78) and Alexander Hamilton Stephens (1812–83).

Dr. Long, a distinguished physician, whose discovery of ether anesthesia in the year 1842 gave him a prominent place among the physicians of his native State and throughout the entire medical profession.

Alexander Hamilton Stephens, lawyer, Member of U.S. House of Representatives, 1843–59; elected to the Confederate Congress and chosen by that Congress as Vice President of the provisional government; Vice President of the Confederacy, 1861–65; imprisoned 5 months at Fort Warren, Massachusetts, after the War; elected to the U.S. Senate but denied admission; author of a comprehensive 2 volume edition, "The War Between the States"; Member of the U.S. House of Representatives, 1873–82; Governor of Georgia, 1882–83, and died while occupying that position.

Idaho—George L. Shoup (1836–1904) and William E. Borah (1865–1940)

George L. Shoup, pioneer, soldier and statesman; delegate to the Colorado Territorial constitutional convention 1864; colonel in the Union Army in the Civil War; Governor of the Idaho Territory, 1889–90; elected first Governor of Idaho, 1890, and resigned to become first U.S. Senator from Idaho, 1890–1901.

William Edgar Borah, lawyer, legislator, and statesman; a great advocate and orator and illustrious for his renown and for his distinguished civic services. Known as the Lone Lion of Idaho. United States Senator from Idaho, 1907–40.

Illinois—James Shields (1810–79) and Frances E. Willard (1839–98)

James Shields was a State supreme court justice; a brigadier general in the War with Mexico, 1846–48 and a Union officer of the same rank in the Civil War, 1861–63; appointed Governor of the Oregon Territory by President Polk and resigned in 1849. He represented 3 States—Illinois, 1849–55, Minnesota, 1858–59, and Missouri, 1879— in the U.S. Senate.

Frances E. Willard, educator, social and economic reformer, orator and journalist. Became president of Evanston College for Ladies, 1871 (later part of Northwestern University); dean and professor of aesthetics at Northwestern; associated in evangelist movement with Dwight Moody; president of Illinois Women's Christian Temperance Union, 1873; elected president of National Woman's Temperance Union, 1879; founder and president of World's Christian Temperance Union, 1883; persuasive orator and journalist. Her contributions to newspapers and magazines consisted chiefly of editing the organs of the society papers and magazines.

Indiana—Oliver P. Morton (1823–77) and General Lew Wallace (1827–1905)

Oliver P. Morton served his State as circuit court judge, Lieutenant Governor, and as one of the greatest war Governors of the Civil War, who supported Lincoln and the Union cause. As a Member of the U.S. Senate, 1867–77, he was a great constructive statesman.

General Wallace succeeded in the careers of lawyer, soldier, diplomat, and author. He served in the War with Mexico and attained the rank of Major General during the Civil War. He served in the Indiana State senate; as territorial Governor of New Mexico; was Minister to Turkey, and was author of the novels, "The Fair God," "Ben Hur" and "The Prince of India."

Iowa—James Harlan (1820–99) and Samuel Jordan Kirkwood (1813–94).

James Harlan was distinguished as a statesman, educator, and orator. Taught at Iowa City College, and worked his way up to State Superintendent of Public Instruction; President of Iowa Wesleyan University, 1853–55. President Johnson appointed him as Secretary of the Interior, 1865–66. His service in the U.S. Senate, 1857–65, and as presiding judge on the Alabama Claims Commission climaxed an already brilliant career. His daughter married Robert Todd Lincoln.

Samuel J. Kirkwood, a lawyer by profession, served as county prosecuting attorney, 1845–49; as a member of the Ohio constitutional convention, 1850–51; of the Iowa State senate, 1856–59; as Governor, 1860–64, 1876–77; as U.S. Senator, 1866–67, 1877–81; and as Secretary of the Interior under President Garfield, 1881–82.

Kansas—John J. Ingalls (1833–1900) and George Washington Glick (1827–1911).

John J. Ingalls' greatest services were to his State as lawyer, scholar, orator and statesman.

He was a delegate to the Kansas constitutional convention; secretary of the Kansas Territorial Council; member of the State senate; secretary of state and served as judge advocate during the Civil War, rising to the rank of lieutenant colonel. Member of the U.S. Senate, 1873–1891, where he was President pro tempore, 1887–1891.

George W. Glick was a lawyer, farmer, statesman, and Governor of the State of Kansas. He was also a soldier in the Union Army in the Civil War; and although he enlisted in the War with Mexico, hostilities had ceased before he saw active service. He was an uncompromising free-State man, and helped to prepare the constitution upon which the State of Kansas was admitted to the Union.

Kentucky—Henry Clay (1777–1852) and Ephraim McDowell (1771–1830).

Henry Clay, lawyer, statesman, parliamentarian, orator—U.S. Senator, 1806–07, (in contravention of the 30-year age requirement of the Constitution) and also served intermittently from 1810 until his death in 1852. Member of the Kentucky legislature, 1808–09; Member of the U.S. House of Representatives intermittently, 1811 to 1825. Chosen to the Speakership the day he became a Member, an unprecedented distinction. Served as Speaker—12th, 13th, 2nd session of 14th, 15th, 1st session 16th, and 18th Congresses. Appointed as Peace Commissioner to Great Britain in 1814; was Secretary of State under John Quincy Adams, 1825–29.

Ephraim McDowell, a renowned physician, graduate of the University of Edinburgh, Scotland; followed the practice of medicine and surgery during his entire professional life, successfully performing the first operation known as Ovariotomy in 1809. He was one of the founders and original trustees of Centre College, Danville, Kentucky; and a member of many medical societies.

Louisiana—Huey Pierce Long (1893–1935) and Edward Douglass White (1845–1921).

Huey P. Long, lawyer, State railroad commissioner; Governor of Louisiana, 1928–1932; U.S. Senator, 1932–1935. He fostered the distribution of free school books and equalized educational opportunities throughout Louisiana; advocated distribution of wealth, pensions for the aged and shorter working hours for labor.

Edward Douglass White was a Confederate soldier, noted jurist, and statesman; at 16 he became a soldier of the Confederate Army; Member of State senate, 1874–1878; associate justice of the State supreme court, 1879–1880; elected U.S. Senator, 1891–1894; appointed Associate Justice of the Supreme Court of the U.S., 1894; and later served as Chief Justice, 1910–1921.

Maine—William King (1768–1852) and Hannibal Hamlin (1809–91)

William King, statesman, Governor, industrialist. Member of the Massachusetts legislature; assisted in securing passage of the Act of Toleration and the Betterment Act (the first step toward religious enfranchisement); attained the rank of Major General of the Maine Militia in the War of 1812. Leader in separating Maine from Massachusetts; President of Maine constitutional convention, 1819 and elected first Governor of Maine in 1820.

Hannibal Hamlin served in legislature of his native State, elected to U.S. House of Representatives, 1843–1847; elected to U.S. Senate, 1848–1857, and resigned to become Governor of Maine, 1857; reelected to U.S. Senate, 1857–1861; resigned to become Vice President of the United States, 1861–1865, under Lincoln. Enlisted as private in the Maine State Guard, Civil War, 1864. Was collector of port of Boston; again to U.S. Senate, 1869–1881, and served two terms. U.S. Minister to Spain and after service from 1881 to 1882, when he resigned, devoted the remainder of his life to agricultural pursuits.

Maryland—Charles Carroll of Carrollton (1737–1832) and John Hanson (1715–83).

Charles Carroll of Carrollton, lawyer, patriot, statesman and Signer of the Declaration of Independence. Educated by French Jesuits; studied law in France and England; was for independence of the colonies; belonged to the council of safety of his State; Commissioner to Canada, 1776; delegate to the Continental Congress, 1776–78; Member of Maryland State senate, 1777–1800. U.S. Senator, 1789–1792; and was the last surviving Signer of the Declaration of Independence.

John Hanson, patriot and statesman; President of the Continental Congress. Patriot of the Revolution; Member of State house of delegates, 9 terms; Member of State senate, 1757–1773; Delegate to General Congress in Annapolis, 1774; Member of Continental Congress, 1780–1783; President of Continental Congress, 1781; Signer of the Articles of Confederation, 1781.

Massachusetts—Samuel Adams (1722–1803) and John Winthrop (1588–1649).

Samuel Adams, lawyer, and patriot of the Revolution; called the "Father of the American Revolution" and Signer of the Declaration of Independence. Opposed the stamp tax; Member of the General Court of Massachusetts, 1765–1774; Member of the Continental Congress, 1774–1782; Member of Massachusetts Constitutional Convention, 1779; President of Massachusetts State senate, 1781; member of the State convention which ratified the U.S. Constitution, 1788; Lieutenant-Governor of Massachusetts, 1789–1794; Governor, 1794–1797.

John Winthrop, Puritan colonizer, author, lawyer; first Governor of Massachusetts Bay Colony, serving 12 years. He believed in evangelizing the Indians, opposed democracy, and believed superior minds, though always in the minority, should rule.

Michigan—Lewis Cass (1782–1866) and Zachariah Chandler (1813–1879).

Lewis Cass served his State and Nation as a soldier, diplomat and statesman. He was a member of the Ohio house of representatives; Brigadier General during the War of 1812; Governor of Territory of Michigan, 1813–1831. He was appointed Secretary of War by President Jackson, 1831–1836; U.S. Minister to France, 1836–42; U.S. Senator, 1845–48, 1849–57; and Secretary of State under President Buchanan, 1857–1860, and an unsuccessful candidate for President. He left the Cabinet of President Buchanan when secession was imminent.

Zachariah Chandler opposed secession and slavery above all else; aided in organizing the Republican Party. As a U.S. Senator, 1857–1875, he became the confidant of Lincoln and steadfastly advocated the principles of his Party. He also served as Secretary of the Interior, 1875–1877, under President Grant.

Minnesota—Henry Mower Rice (1817–1894) and Maria L. Sanford (1836–1920).

Henry Mower Rice was instrumental in securing Minnesota Statehood; a delegate from the Territory; later United States Senator from Minnesota, 1853–63; appointed United States Commissioner to negotiate Indian Treaties, 1887–88.

Maria L. Sanford was a noted woman orator and educator—one of the first women professors in the United States; leader in adult education; founder of early parent-teacher groups; she espoused the education for Negroes, justice for the Indians, and women's rights.

Mississippi—Jefferson Davis (1808–1889) and James Z. George (1826–1897).

Jefferson Davis, soldier, statesman, President of the Confederacy. A graduate of West Point, fought in the Black Hawk War, 1830–31, the War with Mexico, and served as Secretary of War under President Pierce, 1853–1857. As Secretary of War, the erection of the new House and Senate Wings and Dome of the U.S. Capitol came under his jurisdiction. He was also a member of the U.S. House of Representatives, 1845–1846; the U.S. Senate, 1847–1851, 1857–1861, resigning when his State left the Union. In 1862, he was elected President of the Southern Confederacy.

James Z. George, lawyer, soldier in the War with Mexico and Confederate Brigadier General of the Civil War; also attained distinction as chief justice of the State supreme court, 1879 and as a U.S. Senator, 1881–1897. As a leading member of the Mississippi constitutional convention in 1890, he influenced and guided the reestablishment of a sound State government.

Missouri—Thomas H. Benton (1782–1858) and Francis P. Blair, Jr. (1821–1875).

Thomas H. Benton, author, lawyer, statesman; member of the Tennessee legislature, 1809–11; Aide-de-camp to General Jackson in the War of 1812; editor of the "Missouri Inquirer;" U.S. Senator, 1821–1851; member of the U.S. House of Representatives, 1853–1855, and author of "The Thirty Years View," and "Abridgment of the Debates of Congress from 1789–1850." He championed the Western interests and advocated expansionism.

Francis P. Blair, Jr., soldier, lawyer, and statesman; served in War with Mexico. Member of the Missouri general assembly; served in the U.S. House of Representatives intermittently from 1852 to 1864, and the U.S. Senate, 1871–1873. During the Civil War, he served as a Major General and was instrumental in saving his State for the Union.

Montana—Charles Marion Russell (1864–1926)

Charles Marion Russell, known as "The Cowboy Artist," was an illustrator, writer, philosopher, and humorist who faithfully and devotedly recorded the spirit of the Old West.

Nebraska—William Jennings Bryan (1860–1925) and J. Sterling Morton (1832–1902).

William J. Bryan, soldier, lawyer, orator and statesman. Member of the U.S. House of Representatives, 1891–1895; 3 times an unsuccessful candidate for President of the United States; Colonel in the Spanish-American War, 1898; founder of "The Commoner" newspaper, 1901; a zealous worker in religious and civic interests; and served as Secretary of State under President Wilson, 1913–15.

J. Sterling Morton, statesman and Arbor Day Founder. A prominent leader in the early history of Nebraska; Secretary of the Nebraska Territory and acting Governor, 1858–1859; Secretary of Agriculture under President Cleveland, 1893, and widely known for his efforts in the direction of the observance of Arbor Day.

Nevada—Patrick Anthony McCarran (1876–1954).

Patrick Anthony McCarran was a distinguished lawyer and statesman whose opinions as Chief Justice of the Nevada supreme court, 1917–1918, remain valued legal text; elected to the United States Senate in 1932, and served until his death in 1954; was one of the first to advocate a separate United States Air Force.

New Hampshire—John Stark (1728–1822) and Daniel Webster (1782–1852).

John Stark, patriot and soldier. Achieved fame as a courageous and relentless soldier during the French and Indian War, 1754–1763, and the Revolutionary War when he led Washington's advance at Trenton, 1776; headed the New Hampshire troops at the Battle of Bunker Hill, 1775; and won the Battle of Bennington, 1777. He was commissioned a Major General in 1786.

Daniel Webster, Constitutional lawyer, orator and statesman. A native of New Hampshire—that State elected him to the U.S. House of Representatives, 1813–1817. He represented his adopted State of Massachusetts in the U.S. House of Representatives, 1823–1827 and in the U.S. Senate,

1827–1841 and 1845–1850. Secretary of State under Presidents Harrison, Tyler and Fillmore.

New Jersey—Richard Stockton (1730–1781) and Gen. Philip Kearny (1814–1862).

Richard Stockton, lawyer, jurist and Signer of the Declaration of Independence; an important factor upon the side of the Colonies during the Revolution; an associate justice on the New Jersey supreme court, 1774–1776; a member of the Continental Congress, 1776.

General Kearny, "The Perfect Soldier" who was distinguished on two continents for his conspicuous bravery and military accomplishments. He fought in Algiers, 1840; in the War with Mexico, 1848, and as a Major General in the Civil War. In that war he lost his life at Chantilly, Virginia, 1862.

New York—Robert R. Livingston (1746–1813) and George Clinton (1739–1812).

Robert R. Livingston, jurist, diplomat, statesman. Delegate to the Continental Congress, 1775–77, 1779–81; one of committee of 5 who drafted the Declaration of Independence, but did not sign it; Delegate to State Constitutional Convention, 1777; Secretary of Foreign Affairs under the Articles of Confederation. As Chancellor of New York State, he administered the first Presidential oath of office to George Washington, 1789; U.S. Minister to France, 1801–04, and aided in negotiating the Louisiana Purchase; assisted Robert Fulton and his partner in constructing the first steamboat.

George Clinton, lawyer, soldier, Governor and Vice President. Fought in the French and Indian War and as a Brigadier General in the Revolutionary War; delegate to the Continental Congress, 1775; first Governor of New York, 1777–1795, 1801–1804; President of the New York convention ratifying the U.S. Constitution; and Vice President of the United States under both Jefferson and Madison.

North Carolina—Zebulon Baird Vance (1830–94) and Charles Brantley Aycock (1859–1912).

Zebulon B. Vance, soldier, Governor, lawyer, statesman. Member of the State house of commons, 1854; Member of the U.S. House of Representatives, 1858–1861; entered the Confederate Army during the Civil War as a captain, 1861; promoted to a Colonel; Governor of North Carolina, 1862–1866 and 1876–1878; served in the U.S. Senate, 1879–1894.

Charles B. Aycock, lawyer, educator and Governor. Superintendent of Public Instruction, Wayne County, 1881; U.S. district attorney, 1893–1897; Governor of North Carolina, 1901–1905.

North Dakota—John Burke (1859–1937).

John Burke, "North Dakota's Lincoln"; jurist, statesman, Governor, Treasurer of the United States. State representative, 1890; State senator, 1892; Governor of North Dakota, 1906; Treasurer of the United States, 1913–21; Chief Justice of the State supreme court. Under his leadership many corrective laws were placed on the statute books.

Ohio—James A. Garfield (1831–81) and William Allen (1803–79).

James A. Garfield, soldier, lawyer, educator, statesman, President of the United States. Professor and later President of Hiram College, 1857–1861; member of the State senate, 1859; Major General in the Union Army, Civil War; Member of the U.S. House of Representatives, 1863–1880; President of the United States, 1881; assassinated 5 months after his inauguration, and died September 19, 1881.

William Allen, lawyer, statesman, Governor. Member of the U.S. House of Representatives, 1833–1835; member of the U.S. Senate, 1837–1849; Governor, 1874–1876.

Oklahoma—Sequoyah (1770–1845) and Will Rogers (1879–1935).

Sequoyah was a Cherokee Indian whose father was a German trader; a leader in the affairs of his tribe; was a trader, silversmith, blacksmith, philosopher, and the inventor of the Cherokee alphabet.

Will Rogers was a humorist, humanitarian, cowboy, showman, comedian (stage, screen, and radio), actor, author, after-dinner speaker, columnist, commentator, philosopher, world traveler, goodwill ambassador.

Oregon—Reverend Jason Lee (1803–1845) and Dr. John McLoughlin (1784–1857).

Reverend Jason Lee set out for the Oregon territory in 1834 to become the first missionary of this area; in an 1838 petition he urged Congress to, "take formal and speedy possession" of the Oregon Country.

Dr. John McLoughlin often called "the Father of Oregon"; was head of the powerful Hudson's Bay Company in the Pacific Northwest territory, 1824–1845; assisted the missionaries and settlers in what is now Washington and Oregon. Welcomed first colonizing settlers including Reverend Jason Lee and missionaries.

Pennsylvania—John Peter Gabriel Muhlenberg (1746–1807) and Robert Fulton (1765–1815).

J. P. G. Muhlenberg, soldier, clergyman, statesman. Clergyman in Lutheran and Episcopal churches; member of Virginia House of Burgesses, 1774; with Washington—Brandywine to Yorktown, 1777–1781, Revolutionary War; Major General, 1783; Vice President of Pennsylvania Supreme Executive Council, 1785–1787; member of Pennsylvania constitutional convention, 1790; member of U.S. House of Representatives, 1789–1791; 1793–1795; 1799–1801; member of U.S. Senate, 1801; Supervisor of Revenue for Pennsylvania, 1801; collector of Customs, 1802.

Robert Fulton, artist, civil engineer, inventor. Although an artist of merit and an experimenter in submarine mines and torpedoes, he achieved his greatest distinction for the adaptation of steam power as a means of naval propulsion and for the design of the first successful steamboat, the "Clermont." He became a partner of Robert R. Livingston in constructing the first steamboat.

Rhode Island—Roger Williams (1603/06–1682/83) and General Nathanael Greene (1742–1786).

Roger Williams, colonizer, minister, founder of Rhode Island. Born in England, came to America, 1631; pastor of the Puritan Church at Salem, Massachusetts; banished from the Massachusetts colony in 1635; founded Rhode Island, 1636, and secured the charter for the Providence Plantations, 1644. He was the author of the great declaration of the principle of religious liberty and freedom in the organization of the State. He was one of the earliest of the fathers of American democracy. This statue was the second to be placed in Statuary Hall, 1872.

General Greene, deputy, General Assembly, 1770–72, 1775; Major General, 1776 in the Revolutionary War; was engaged in many major campaigns; acclaimed the "Savior of the South".

His was the first statue to be placed in Statuary Hall, 1870. Rhode Island was the first State to present two statues.

South Carolina—John C. Calhoun (1782–1850) and Wade Hampton (1818–1902)

John C. Calhoun, lawyer, statesman, orator and Vice President of the United States. He was the leader of a school of earnest men who believed secession was warranted or at least permissible under the Constitution of the United States because not expressly forbidden. Member of the State house of representatives, 1808–1809; United States House of Representatives, 1811–1817; Secretary of War under President Monroe, 1817–1825; Vice President of the United States, 1825–1832, under Presidents John Quincy Adams and Andrew Jackson; United States Senator, 1832–1843, 1845–1850; Secretary of State under President Tyler, 1844–1845.

Wade Hampton, soldier, statesman, lawyer, Governor. Member of the State senate, 1858–1862; served in the Confederate Army during the Civil War, commanding "Hampton's Legion;" rose to rank of Lieutenant General (1865) commanding the Cavalry of the Army of Northern Virginia. He was Governor of South Carolina, 1876–1879, and United States Senator, 1879–1891.

South Dakota—Brigadier General William Henry Harrison Beadle (1838–1915) and Joseph Ward (1838–1889).

General Beadle, educator, conservationist, lawyer, and soldier. Through his leadership 20 million acres of school lands were saved for posterity in South Dakota, North Dakota, Montana, Washington, Idaho and Wyoming; he was territorial superintendent of public instruction, 1879, and president of Madison Normal School. He joined the Union forces during the Civil War and rose to brigadier general, receiving three brevet commissions, the first for "gallantry in the defense of Washington City."

Joseph Ward, educator, churchman, and statesman. He began his teaching career at age 17 in a school in western New York. He organized Yankton Academy, 1872; founded Yankton College, 1881; drafted a code of school laws for the Dakota Territory. During the Civil War, Ward served in the Union Army. He was ordained a missionary, 1869; regarded as the father of Congregationalism in the Dakotas. Outstanding leader in the struggle for South Dakota Statehood; author of State Constitution as adopted; composed the state motto, "Under God the people rule," and the Great Seal of South Dakota is the result of his written description of this emblem.

Tennessee—Andrew Jackson (1767–1845) and John Sevier (1745–1815).

Andrew Jackson, soldier, statesman, lawyer, justice and President of the United States. "Old Hickory." An attorney by profession; was a Member of the U.S. House of Representatives (3 months), 1796–1797; United States Senate, 1797–1798; and justice of the Tennessee supreme court, 1798–1804. At age 13, he served in the Revolutionary War; the Creek War, 1813–1814; during the War of 1812 rose to rank of major general; hero of the Battle of New Orleans; commanded the expedition which captured Florida, 1817; became Governor of Florida, 1821. Served again in the United States Senate from Tenn., 1823–1825. Elected President of the United States in 1828. "Old Hickory's" election as President ushered in the era of Jacksonian Democracy—the epoch of the plain people.

John Sevier, soldier, statesman, Frontier leader. He was a Captain of Colonial Militia in Governor Dunmore's War against the Indians, 1773–1774, serving under George Washington; county and district judge, 1777–1780. He won prominence in the Revolutionary War, especially in the Battle of Kings Mountain, 1780. Elected Governor of the proclaimed "State of Franklin," 1785–1788, (which later became Tennessee) and served as the first Governor of the State of Tennessee, 1796–1801, and 1803–1809. Member of the U.S. House of Representatives from North Carolina to the First Congress, 1789–1791 and in 1811 returned to the House as a member from Tennessee and served until his death in 1815.

Texas—Stephen F. Austin (1793–1836) and Samuel Houston (1793–1863).

Stephen F. Austin, colonizer, patriot. Austin carried forward his father's efforts of 1821 in colonizing Texas. Under a contract with Mexico, was given judicial and military control of the local Mexican State of Texas. He assisted in bringing about the recognition of Texan independence, 1836. As Secretary of the Lone Star Republic of Texas he

paved the way for annexation to the United States but did not live to see it accomplished.

Samuel Houston, liberator, soldier, statesman, Governor. His illustrious military career included service as a private in the 39th Regiment, United States Infantry; served under General Jackson in the Creek War, 1818, and later as commander in chief of the Texas Army; led the Texans against Santa Ana and the Mexicans in the Battle of San Jacinto, 1836, thus assuring the independence of Texas.

Houston was a lawyer, district attorney and adjutant general of the State of Tennessee, 1820. He was elected a Member of the U.S. House of Representatives from Tennessee, 1823–1827; Governor of Tennessee, 1827–1829. Moved to Texas; led Texas forces against Mexico, winning independence; first President of Republic of Texas, 1841–1844; took first steps toward annexation of Texas; Senator from State of Texas, 1846–1859; Governor of Texas, 1859–1861; deposed as he refused to take the oath of allegiance to the Confederate States.

Utah—Brigham Young (1801–1877).

Brigham Young, pioneer, empire builder. He was one of the first pioneers to enter Salt Lake Valley in 1847; preeminent in the settling and establishing of the Territory of Deseret, now the State of Utah; and was one of the Territory's most illustrious leaders as a churchman, a Territorial Governor, and a leader of the people in the many trying situations in the early days of the Territory. President of the Mormon Church.

Vermont—Ethan Allen (1737/38–1789) and Jacob Collamer (1792–1865).

Ethan Allen, Revolutionary soldier and author. Served in the French and Indian War; Colonel of the Green Mountain Boys, 1770; won fame in the Revolutionary War as demanding and receiving the surrender of Fort Ticonderoga, 1775; rose to rank of Brigadier General in the Vermont Militia. He prepared Vermont for admission into the Federal Union, finally accomplished two years after his death. He authored many books and articles.

Jacob Collamer, soldier, orator, jurist, statesman. Served in the War of 1812; Member of the State house of representatives, 1821–1822; 1827–1828; States attorney, 1822–1824; Judge of the Superior Court, 1833–1842; 1850–1854; elected to United

States House of Representatives, 1843–1849; Postmaster General under President Taylor, 1849–1850; United States Senator, 1855–1865.

Virginia—George Washington (1732–1799) and General Robert E. Lee (1807–1870).

George Washington's accomplishments as delegate to the First and Second Continental Congresses, as commander in chief of the Colonial forces, as President of the Constitutional Convention, and as First President of the United States, accord him a place in history and in the heart's of his compatriots as "The Father of His Country."

Robert E. Lee, a graduate of West Point, 1829, and superintendent, 1852, has been immortalized due to his command of the Army of Northern Virginia during the Civil War. Following his heroic surrender to General Grant at Appomattox, he became President of Washington College at Lexington, Virginia, now named Washington and Lee University in his honor. He also served in the War with Mexico, 1847.

Washington—Marcus Whitman (1802–1847).

Marcus Whitman, doctor, missionary, pioneer, farmer. A courageous medical missionary in the Washington Territory; in 1836 he led a party to the Oregon Territory and settled in Waiilatpu near the present city of Walla Walla, Washington. He assisted the "Great Emigration" of 1843, the first large movement of settlers to the northwest, and which was an important factor in securing the territory for the United States. In the course of his work he with his wife Narcissa, were massacred by the Indians in 1847.

West Virginia—John E. Kenna (1848–1893) and Francis H. Pierpont (1814–1899).

John E. Kenna, soldier, lawyer, statesman. He enlisted in the Confederate Army in 1864 and was wounded in action; elected prosecuting attorney Kanawha County, 1872–1877; judge pro tem, circuit court of his home county, 1875; Member of the U.S. House of Representatives, 1877–1883; U.S. Senate, 1883 until his death in 1893.

Francis H. Pierpont, patriot, statesman, Governor. In 1861, Pierpont was chosen by a staunch Union convention as Provisional Governor of Virginia, when the State officials declared support for the Confederacy. He was elected Governor of Virginia in 1863, serving until 1868. Ironically, he never held the Governorship of West Virginia, even though he steadfastly led the movement which effected the severance of West Virginia from Virginia and the State's admittance into the Union in 1863. He was known as one of the war governors and assisted in the mobilization and sending to the front of more than 40,000 Union troops during the war.

Wisconsin—Robert M. La Follette, Sr. (1855–1925) and Pere James (Jacques) Marquette (1637–1675).

Robert La Follette, lawyer, statesman, Governor; was district attorney, Dane County, 1880–1884; Member of the United States House of Representatives, 1885–1891; Governor of Wisconsin, 1901–1906; resigned on election to the United States Senate where he served from 1906 until his death in 1925. He wrote into the law of the land many constructive measures designed to safeguard the liberties and economic interest of the workers.

Pere Marquette, pioneer, explorer and missionary. Marquette was a French Jesuit priest, a missionary among the wild tribes of Indians of the northern country. He established missions there, and his missions at Sault Ste. Marie and Mackinaw became the sites of the first towns in Michigan. Included in his explorations with Louis Joliet in 1673 was the course of the Mississippi River which led to the discovery of the waterway to the Gulf of Mexico. He died on the return trip in 1675 near what is now Ludington, Michigan and was buried in Mackinaw. Though only 38 years of age his explorations and his work among the Indians are recognized all over the civilized world. Although not a native of Wisconsin or a citizen of that State, the right of that State to commemorate the services of Marquette was established by a joint resolution of Congress approved October 21, 1893.

Wyoming—Esther Hobart Morris (1813/14–1902).

Mrs. Morris, judge, mother of woman suffrage in Wyoming, was a convincing proponent and advocate of laws granting voting and office holding privileges to the women of the Wyoming territory; such laws were enacted in 1869. She was the first woman to hold the office of justice of the peace, and no decision of hers was ever reversed by a higher court on appeal.

225

SAMUEL ADAMS, Massachusetts
Marble statue by Anne Whitney.
Location: Statuary Hall.

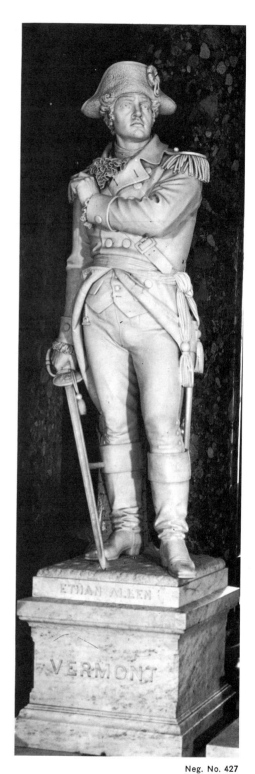

ETHAN ALLEN, Vermont
Marble statue by Larkin G. Mead.
Location: Statuary Hall.

WILLIAM ALLEN, Ohio
Marble statue by Charles H. Niehaus.
Location: Statuary Hall.

STEPHEN F. AUSTIN, Texas
Marble statue by Elisabet Ney.
Location: Vestibule south of Rotunda.

Neg. No. 444

CHARLES B. AYCOCK, North Carolina
Bronze statue by Charles Keck.
Location: Hall of Columns, first floor, House wing.

Neg. No. 162

WILLIAM H. H. BEADLE, South Dakota
Bronze statue by H. Daniel Webster.
Location: Statuary Hall.

228

THOMAS H. BENTON, Missouri
Marble statue by Alexander Doyle.
Location: Statuary Hall.

FRANCIS P. BLAIR, JR., Missouri
Marble statue by Alexander Doyle.
Location: Hall of Columns, first floor, House wing.

Neg. No. 163

Neg. No. 12

WILLIAM E. BORAH, Idaho
Bronze statue by Bryant Baker.
Location: Senate Connection.

WILLIAM J. BRYAN, Nebraska
Bronze statue by Rudulph Evans.
Location: Statuary Hall.

Neg. No. 27440

JOHN BURKE, North Dakota
Bronze statue by Avard Fairbanks.
Location: Statuary Hall.

Neg. No. 27588

JOHN C. CALHOUN, South Carolina
Marble statue by Frederic W. Ruckstull.
Location: Statuary Hall.

Neg. No. 23358

CHARLES CARROLL OF CARROLLTON, Maryland
Bronze statue by Richard E. Brooks.
Location: Statuary Hall.

Neg. No. 27492

LEWIS CASS, Michigan
Marble statue by Daniel C. French.
Location: Statuary Hall.

ZACHARIAH CHANDLER, Michigan
Marble statue by Charles H. Niehaus.
Location: Hall of Columns, first floor, House wing.

JAMES P. CLARKE, Arkansas
Marble statue by Pompeo Coppini.
Location: Hall of Columns, first floor, House wing.

39–071 O—65——17

Neg. No. 408

Neg. No. 27493

HENRY CLAY, Kentucky
Bronze statue by Charles H. Niehaus.
Location: Statuary Hall.

JOHN M. CLAYTON, Delaware
Marble statue by Bryant Baker.
Location: Senate Connection.

Neg. No. 452

Neg. No. 28002

GEORGE CLINTON, New York
Bronze statue by Henry Kirke Brown.
Location: Vestibule south of Rotunda.

JACOB COLLAMER, Vermont
Marble Statue by Preston Powers.
Location: Hall of Columns, first floor, House wing.

235

Neg. No. 28003

JABEZ LAMAR MONROE CURRY, Alabama
Marble statue by Dante Sodini.
Location: Hall of Columns, first floor, House wing.

Neg. No. 414

JEFFERSON DAVIS, Mississippi
Bronze statue by Augustus Lukeman.
Location: Statuary Hall.

ROBERT FULTON, Pennsylvania
Marble statue by Howard Roberts.
Location: Statuary Hall.

JAMES A. GARFIELD, Ohio
Marble statue by Charles H. Niehaus.
Location: Rotunda.

JAMES Z. GEORGE, Mississippi
Bronze statue by Augustus Lukeman.
Location: Hall of Columns, first floor, House wing.

238

Neg. No. 438

GEORGE W. GLICK, Kansas
Marble statue by Charles H. Niehaus.
Location: Hall of Columns, first floor, House wing.

Neg. No. 27494

JOHN GORRIE, Florida
Marble statue by C. Adrian Pillars.
Location: Statuary Hall.

Neg. No. 27451

Neg. No. 397

NATHANAEL GREENE, Rhode Island
Marble statue by H. K. Brown.
Location: Vestibule of former Supreme Court Room.

JOHN C. GREENWAY, Arizona
Bronze statue by Gutzon Borglum.
Location: Statuary Hall.

HANNIBAL HAMLIN, Maine
Bronze statue by Charles E. Tefft.
Location: Statuary Hall.

WADE HAMPTON, South Carolina
Marble statue by Frederic W. Ruckstull.
Location: House Connection.

JOHN HANSON, Maryland
Bronze statue by Richard E. Brooks.
Location: Senate Connection.

JAMES HARLAN, Iowa
Bronze statue by Nellie V. Walker.
Location: Hall of Columns, first floor, House wing.

SAMUEL HOUSTON, Texas
Marble statue by Elisabet Ney.
Location: Statuary Hall.

JOHN J. INGALLS, Kansas
Marble statue by Charles H. Niehaus.
Location: Statuary Hall.

243

ANDREW JACKSON, Tennessee
Bronze statue by Belle Kinney Scholz and Leopold F.
Scholz.
Location: Rotunda.

PHILIP KEARNY, New Jersey
Bronze statue by Henry Kirke Brown.
Location: Hall of Columns, first floor House wing.

Neg. No. 433

THOMAS STARR KING, California
Bronze statue by Haig Patigian.
Location: Hall of Columns, first floor, House wing.

Neg. No. 28004

JOHN E. KENNA, West Virginia
Marble statue by Alexander Doyle.
Location: Hall of Columns, first floor, House wing.

WILLIAM KING, Maine
Marble Statue by Franklin Simmons.
Location: House Connection.

SAMUEL J. KIRKWOOD, Iowa
Bronze statue by Vinnie Ream Hoxie.
Location: Statuary Hall.

ROBERT M. LA FOLLETTE, Sr. Wisconsin
Marble statue by Jo Davidson.
Location: Statuary Hall.

REV. JASON LEE, Oregon
Bronze statue by G. MacG. Proctor.
Location: Statuary Hall.

Neg. No. 429

ROBERT E. LEE, Virginia
Bronze statue by Edward V. Valentine.
Location: Statuary Hall.

Neg. No. 418

ROBERT R. LIVINGSTON, New York
Bronze statue by Erastus Dow Palmer.
Location: Statuary Hall.

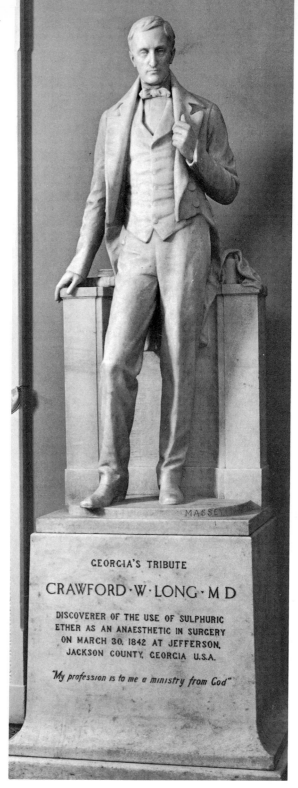

Dr. CRAWFORD W. LONG, Georgia
Marble statue by J. Massey Rhind.
Location: Senate Connection.

HUEY P. LONG, Louisiana
Bronze statue by Charles Keck.
Location: Statuary Hall.

Neg. No. 27452
JAMES MARQUETTE (Pere Jacques), Wisconsin
Marble statue by Gaetano Trentanove.
Location: House Connection.

Neg. No. 27455
PATRICK McCARRAN, Nevada
Bronze statue by Yolande Jacobson (Mrs. J. Craig Sheppard).
Location: Small vestibule adjacent to Statuary Hall.

250

Neg. No. 161

Neg. No. 27497

DR. JOHN McLOUGHLIN, Oregon
Bronze statue by Gifford Proctor.
Location: House Connection.

Dr. EPHRAIM McDOWELL, Kentucky
Bronze statue by Charles H. Niehaus.
Location: Senate Connection.

Neg. No. 27442

Neg. No. 85

ESTHER H. MORRIS, Wyoming
Bronze statue by Avard Fairbanks.
Location: Small vestibule adjacent to Statuary Hall.

J. STERLING MORTON, Nebraska
Bronze statue by Rudulph Evans.
Location: Hall of Columns, first floor, House wi

Neg. No. 27522

Neg. No. 450

OLIVER P. MORTON, Indiana
Marble statue by Charles H. Niehaus.
Location: Hall of Columns, first floor, House wing.

J. P. G. MUHLENBERG, Pennsylvania
Marble statue by Blanche Nevin.
Location: Vestibule south of Rotunda.

FRANCIS H. PIERPONT, West Virginia
Marble statue by Franklin Simmons.
Location: Statuary Hall.

HENRY MOWER RICE, Minnesota
Marble statue by Frederick E. Triebel.
Location: Statuary Hall.

Neg. No. 27435

Neg. No. 113

CAESAR RODNEY, Delaware
Marble statue by Bryant Baker.
Location: Statuary Hall.

WILL ROGERS, Oklahoma
Bronze statue by Jo Davidson.
Location: House Connection.

Neg. No. 23357

URIAH M. ROSE, Arkansas
Marble statue by Frederic W. Ruckstull.
Location: Statuary Hall.

Neg. No. 27438

CHARLES M. RUSSELL, Montana
Bronze statue by John B. Weaver.
Location: Statuary Hall.

Neg. No. 14662

DR. FLORENCE RENA SABIN, Colorado
Bronze statue by Joy Buba.
Location: Statuary Hall.

Neg. No. 27499

MARIA L. SANFORD, Minnesota
Bronze statue by Evelyn Raymond.
Location: Senate Connection.

Neg. No. 421

Neg. No. 398

SEQUOYAH (SEQUOYA), Oklahoma
Bronze statue by Vinnie Ream Hoxie.
Location: Statuary Hall.

JUNIPERO SERRA, California
Bronze statue by Ettore Cadorin.
Location: Statuary Hall.

258

Neg. No. 425

Neg. No. 399

JOHN SEVIER, Tennessee
Bronze statue by Belle Kinney Scholz and Leopold F. Scholz.
Location: Statuary Hall.

ROGER SHERMAN, Connecticut
Marble statue by Chauncey B. Ives.
Location: Statuary Hall.

Neg. No. 27520

GENERAL JAMES SHIELDS, Illinois
Bronze statue by Leonard W. Volk.
Location: Hall of Columns, first floor, House wing.

Neg. No. 27852

GEORGE L. SHOUP, Idaho
Marble statue by Frederick E. Triebel.
Location: Statuary Hall.

GENERAL EDMUND KIRBY SMITH, Florida
Bronze statue by Charles A. Pillars.
Location: Hall of Columns, first floor, House wing.

JOHN STARK, New Hampshire
Marble statue by Carl Conrads.
Location: Vestibule of former Supreme Court Room.

261

ALEXANDER H. STEPHENS, Georgia
Marble statue by Gutzon Borglum.
Location: Statuary Hall.

RICHARD STOCKTON, New Jersey
Marble statue by H. K. Brown.
Location: Statuary Hall.

Neg. No. 27436

JONATHAN TRUMBULL, Connecticut
Marble statue by Chauncey B. Ives.
Location: House Connection.

Neg. No. 419

ZEBULON BAIRD VANCE, North Carolina
Bronze statue by Gutzon Borglum.
Location: Statuary Hall.

Neg. No. 405

GENERAL LEW WALLACE, Indiana
Marble statue by Andrew O'Connor.
Location: Statuary Hall.

Neg. No. 25967

JOSEPH WARD, South Dakota
Marble statue by Bruno Beghe.
Location: Hall of Columns, first floor, House wing.

264

GEORGE WASHINGTON, Virginia
Bronze statue by William Hubard (after Houdon).
Location: Rotunda.

DANIEL WEBSTER, New Hampshire
Marble statue by Carl Conrads.
Location: Statuary Hall.

39–071 O—65——19

GENERAL JOSEPH WHEELER, Alabama
Bronze statue by Berthold Nebel.
Location: Statuary Hall.

EDWARD DOUGLASS WHITE, Louisiana
Bronze statue by Arthur C. Morgan.
Location: Senate connection.

MARCUS WHITMAN, Washington
Bronze statue by Avard Fairbanks.
Location: Statuary Hall.

FRANCES E. WILLARD, Illinois
Marble statue by Helen F. Mears.
Location: Statuary Hall.

ROGER WILLIAMS, Rhode Island
Marble statue by Franklin Simmons.
Location: Statuary Hall.

JOHN WINTHROP, Massachusetts
Marble statue by Richard S. Greenough.
Location: Hall of Columns, first floor, House wing.

BRIGHAM YOUNG, Utah
Marble statue by Mahonri Young.
Location: Statuary Hall.

Statues in the United States Capitol Not Contributed by States

Eight Statues, Not Contributed by States, Have Been Acquired and Made Part of the Capitol Art Collection:

EDWARD DICKINSON BAKER, Member of the U.S. House of Representatives, 1845–1846; 1849–1851; Member of the U.S. Senate, 1860; Major General in the Civil War and killed at Balls Bluff, 1861. Marble statue by Horatio Stone, acquired by purchase in 1873, located in the Rotunda.

BENJAMIN FRANKLIN, marble statue by Hiram Powers, acquired by purchase (contract 1859), placed 1862, located in Senate wing, east corridor, second floor.

GENERAL ULYSSES S. GRANT, marble statue by Franklin Simmons, accepted by Public Resolution 34, approved August 14, 1890, as a gift from the Grand Army of the Republic, located in the Rotunda.

ALEXANDER HAMILTON, marble statue by Horatio Stone, acquired by purchase, 1866–1868, placed 1868, located in the Rotunda.

JOHN HANCOCK, marble statue by Horatio Stone, acquired by purchase in 1857–1861, located in Senate wing, west corridor, second floor.

THOMAS JEFFERSON, bronze statue by David d'Angers, presented as a gift by Lieutenant Uriah P. Levy, United States Navy, in 1834. For some time it occupied a place in the Rotunda of the United States Capitol. By resolution of February 16, 1835, the statue was ordered removed from the Rotunda "to some suitable place for its preservation until final disposition of it be determined by Congress." By order of President James K. Polk, the statue was erected on the grounds north of the Executive Mansion. There it remained until 1874, when it was returned to Statuary Hall in the United States Capitol. In 1900 it was placed once more in the Rotunda.

THOMAS JEFFERSON, marble statue by Hiram Powers, acquired by purchase (contract 1859) placed 1863, located in House wing, east corridor, second floor.

ABRAHAM LINCOLN, marble statue by Vinnie Ream (Hoxie), acquired by purchase in 1871, located in the Rotunda.

ARD DICKINSON BAKER
ble statue by Horatio Stone.
Location: Rotunda.

BENJAMIN FRANKLIN
Marble statue by Hiram Powers.
Location: Senate wing, second floor, east corridor.

Neg. No. 484

Neg. No. 483

Gen. ULYSSES S. GRANT
Marble statue by Franklin Simmons.
Location: Rotunda.

ALEXANDER HAMILTON
Marble statue by Horatio Stone.
Location: Rotunda.

272

Neg. No. 26688

JOHN HANCOCK
Marble statue by Horatio Stone.
Location: Senate wing, second floor, west corridor.

THOMAS JEFFERSON
Marble statue by Hiram Powers.
Location: House wing, east corridor, second floor.

Neg. No. 482–A

Neg. No. 24567

THOMAS JEFFERSON
Bronze statue by David d'Angers.
Location: Rotunda.

ABRAHAM LINCOLN
Marble statue by Vinnie Ream (Hoxie).
Location: Rotunda.

Statue of Liberty and the Eagle

LIBERTY, plaster statue standing in the niche high above the entablature on the south wall of Statuary Hall, by Enrico Causici, replaced (1817–1819) the Liberty Statue by Giuseppe Franzoni, which was destroyed by the fire of 1814. On the right side of the figure is the frustrum of a column serving as an altar, around which the serpent, the emblem of wisdom, is entwined. On her right is the American Eagle.

LIBERTY and the EAGLE
Plaster statue by Enrico Causici.
Location: in the niche above the entablature on the south wall of Statuary Hall.

Neg. No. 11748

Sculptured Marble Portrait Monument

MEMORIAL TO THE PIONEERS OF THE WOMEN'S SUFFRAGE MOVEMENT

Portrait Monument of Elizabeth Cady Stanton (1815–1902), Susan B. Anthony (1820–1906) and Lucretia Mott (1793–1880) Sculptured By Adelaide Johnson.

This portrait monument located in the Crypt of the Capitol was accepted as a gift from the Women of the United States by the Joint Committee on the Library, February 15, 1921, at ceremonies held in the Rotunda of the Capitol. The block of marble from which these busts are carved is probably as fine a specimen of Carrara marble as ever found place in the Capitol. The estimated weight of the sculpture is between seven and eight tons.

In accepting the monument the Joint Committee on the Library directed that it be placed temporarily in the Rotunda for the purpose of appropriate ceremonies of tender and reception and at the conclusion of the ceremonies, the said sculpture be placed in the Crypt on the first floor of the Capitol beneath the Dome. The date of moving the portrait monument from the Rotunda to the Crypt was May 1921.

SCULPTURED MARBLE PORTRAIT MONUMENT to Elizabeth Cady Stanton, Susan B. Anthony and Lucretia Mott
Executed by Adelaide Johnson.
Location: Crypt, first floor.

Neg. No. 27850

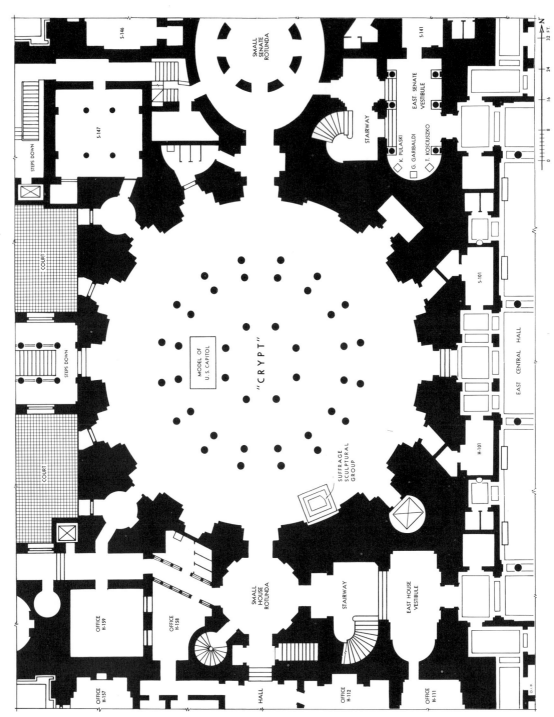

Plan of Central Rotunda (Crypt), 1st (Ground) Floor, Showing Location of Sculptured Portrait Monument of Pioneers of Women's Suffrage Movement and the Model of the U.S. Capitol.

Twenty-three Relief Portraits of Lawgivers in Marble Over Gallery Doors, House Chamber

During the remodeling of the House of Representatives Chamber in 1949-50, there were placed over the gallery doors in the House Chamber 23 relief portraits in marble of men noted in history for the part they have played in the evolution of what has become American law.

These great lawgivers, in chronological order, are:

Hammurabi, the First King of Babylonia, Reigned About 2067-2025 B. C.

The great law code bearing his name is recognized in legal literature as, perhaps, the earliest surviving code, characterized by its primitiveness.

Moses—Circa 1571-1451 B. C.

Hebrew prophet and lawgiver. Amongst all lawgivers, founders of states and teachers of mankind, none has excelled Moses, who transformed a horde of slaves and wanderers into a nation, disciplined a race, and breathed into it its character. To him is attributed the delivery of the Ten Commandments.

Lycurgus—Circa 900 B. C.

Legislator, traditional author of laws and institutions of Sparta (by present standards a harsh code).

Solon—Circa 594 B. C.

The great Athenian lawgiver, author of constitutional and legal reforms.

Gaius—Circa 110-180 A. D.

A celebrated Roman jurist, probably a native of the Eastern Empire. He was the author of numerous works on the civil law, the most noted being "The Institutes."

Papinian—Circa 200 A. D.

A Roman, remarkable not only for his juridical genius, for his independence of judgment, lucidity and firmness, but for his sense of right and morality by which he frequently rose above the barriers of national prejudices, and merited the highest veneration of succeeding centuries.

Justinian—483-565 A. D.

One of the most important events of the reign of this Byzantine emperor was the publication of the Justinian Code, the body of the Roman law compiled and annotated, the most important of all monuments of jurisprudence.

Tribonian—Circa 500-547 A. D.

A Byzantine jurist, he was head of the commission which codified the laws under Justinian.

Maimonides—1135-1204 A. D.

Jewish philosopher of Cordova, he compiled a systematic exposition of the whole of Jewish law as contained in the Pentateuch and in Talmudic literature.

Gregory IX—Circa 1147-1241 A. D.

Author of a compilation of decretals on canon law; during a critical period he accomplished much in maintaining the remnants of Roman law.

Innocent III—1161-1216 A. D.

A profound student of canon and civil law, his accomplishments during a dark and critical period of human history were much the same as those of Gregory IX—preservation of the remnants of Roman law

Simon de Montfort—1200-1265 A.D.

Celebrated English statesman, he originated the first appearance of the House of Commons of England.

St. Louis—1214-1270 A.D.

King of France, author of the Mise of Amiens.

Alphonso X, the "Wise"—1221-1284 A.D.

King of Leon and Castile, he was the author of the code "Las Siete Partidas," the basis of Spanish jurisprudence.

Edward I—1239-1307 A.D.

King of England, founder of the parliamentary constitution of England and eliminator of feudalism from political life. "What touches all should be approved by all, and common dangers should be met by measures agreed upon in common."

Suleiman—1494–1566 A.D.

"The lawgiver," Sultan of Turkey, reformer and improver of civil and military codes. "His amelioration of the lot of his Christian subjects is not his least title to fame."

Grotius—1583–1645 A.D.

Dutch statesman, Advocate-General of Holland and Zeeland. Author of "De Jure Belli et Pacis," first treatise on international law.

Colbert—1619–1683 A.D.

French statesman, codifier of the ordinances, reformer of the French legal system.

Pothier—1699–1772 A.D.

French jurist, author of Digest of the Pandects. He assembled and codified the remnants of Roman law, and the prevalent French law.

Blackstone—1723–1780 A.D.

A celebrated English jurist, professor of common law at Oxford; his "Commentaries on the Laws of England" had considerable influence on the importation and adaptation of English common law in this country.

George Mason—1726–1792 A.D.

He drafted the Virginia Declaration of Rights, 1776; was a member of the Constitutional Convention in 1787, but led opposition to the ratification of the Constitution until the Bill of Rights was inserted in it.

Napoleon—1769–1821 A.D.

He appointed a commission which produced the "Code Napoleon," and saw that it was enforced. It is prevailing law, even now, in Louisiana, quite influential in Florida, New Mexico, and California.

Thomas Jefferson—1743–1826 A.D.

Third President of the United States, he was author of the Declaration of Independence and of the Statute of Virginia for Religious Freedom.

Sculptors of Relief Portraits Over House Gallery Doors

The relief portraits in marble of great lawgivers, located over the House Gallery doors, are the works of the following artists:

Lawgivers	Sculptors	Carvers
Lycurgus, Grotius, Napoleon, Jefferson	C. Paul Jennewein, New York City	Edward H. Ratti
Gaius, Innocent III, Pothier, Suleiman	Joseph Kiselewski, New York City	Edward H. Ratti
Tribonian, Solon, Maimonides	Brenda Putnam, New York City	Arthur E. Lorenzani
Edward I, Papinian, Colbert	Laura Gardin Fraser, Westport, Conn	Robert C. Wakeman
Alphonso X the "Wise", Mason, Simon de Montfort, Justinian	Gaetano Cecere, Fredericksburg, Va	Bruno Mankowski
Gregory IX, Blackstone, Hammurabi	Thomas Hudson Jones, Washington, D.C.	Bruno Mankowski
Moses, St. Louis	Jean de Marco, New York City	Bruno Mankowski

The work of these seven sculptors was coordinated by Lee Lawrie*, sculptor, of Easton, Md., who supervised the modeling and carving of the portraits.

*Deceased.

The plaster models of these relief portraits are located on the walls of the Rayburn House Office Building Terminal of the House Subway.

Diagrammatic Plan of Gallery of House of Representatives Chamber, 3d (Gallery) Floor, Showing Location of Relief Portraits of Lawgivers.

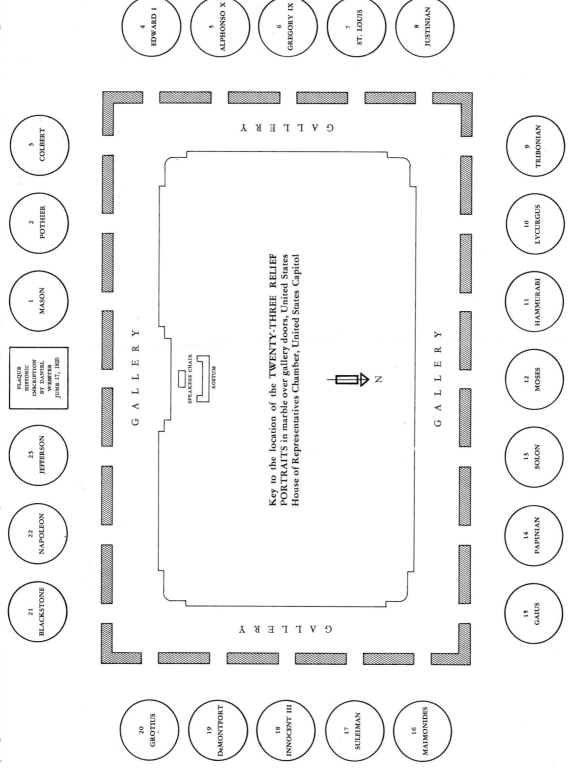

Key to the location of the **TWENTY-THREE RELIEF PORTRAITS** in marble over gallery doors, United States House of Representatives Chamber, United States Capitol

4 EDWARD I
5 ALPHONSO X
6 GREGORY IX
7 ST. LOUIS
8 JUSTINIAN
9 TRIBONIAN
10 LYCURGUS
11 HAMMURABI
12 MOSES
13 SOLON
14 PAPINIAN
15 GAIUS
16 MAIMONIDES
17 SULEIMAN
18 INNOCENT III
19 DeMONTFORT
20 GROTIUS
21 BLACKSTONE
22 NAPOLEON
23 JEFFERSON
1 MASON
2 POTHIER
3 COLBERT

PLAQUE HISTORIC INSCRIPTION BY DANIEL WEBSTER JUNE 17, 1825

GALLERY

SPEAKERS CHAIR

ROSTUM

N

Neg. No. 594

ALPHONSO X, THE "WISE", King of Leon and Castile
Relief portrait by Gaetano Cecere.
Location: House Chamber, above gallery doors.

Neg. No. 595

BLACKSTONE
Relief portrait by Thomas Hudson Jones.
Location: House Chamber, above gallery doors.

COLBERT
Relief portrait by Laura Gardin Fraser.
Location: House Chamber, above gallery doors.

Neg. No. 596

SIMON DE MONTFORT
Relief portrait by Gaetano Cecere.
Location: House Chamber, above gallery doors.

Neg. No. 597

Neg. No. 598

EDWARD I, King of England
Relief portrait by Laura Gardin Fraser.
Location: House Chamber, above gallery doors.

Neg. No. 599

GAIUS
Relief portrait by Joseph Kiselewski.
Location: House Chamber, above gallery doors.

GREGORY IX
Relief portrait by Thomas Hudson Jones.
Location: House Chamber, above gallery doors.

Neg. No. 600

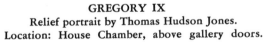

GROTIUS
Relief portrait by C. Paul Jennewein.
Location: House Chamber, above gallery doors.

Neg. No. 601

Neg. No. 602

HAMMURABI, King of Babylonia
Relief portrait by Thomas Hudson Jones.
Location: House Chamber, above gallery doors.

Neg. No. 603

INNOCENT III
Relief portrait by Joseph Kiselewski.
Location: House Chamber, above gallery doors.

THOMAS JEFFERSON
Relief portrait by C. Paul Jennewein.
Location: House Chamber, above gallery doors.
Neg. No. 604

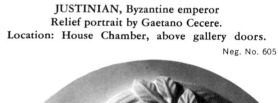

JUSTINIAN, Byzantine emperor
Relief portrait by Gaetano Cecere.
Location: House Chamber, above gallery doors.
Neg. No. 605

Neg. No. 606

LYCURGUS
Relief portrait by C. Paul Jennewein.
Location: House Chamber, above gallery doors.

Neg. No. 607

MAIMONIDES, Jewish philosopher of Cordova
Relief portrait by Brenda Putnam.
Location: House Chamber, above gallery doors.

GEORGE MASON
Relief portrait by Gaetano Cecere.
Location: House Chamber, above gallery doors.

Neg. No. 608

MOSES, Hebrew prophet
Relief portrait by Jean de Marco.
Location: House Chamber, above gallery doors.

Neg. No. 609

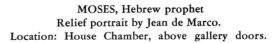

Neg. No. 610

NAPOLEON
Relief portrait by C. Paul Jennewein.
Location: House Chamber, above gallery doors.

Neg. No. 611

PAPINIAN
Relief portrait by Laura Gardin Fraser.
Location: House Chamber, above gallery doors.

POTHIER
Relief portrait by Joseph Kiselewski.
Location: House Chamber, above gallery doors.

Neg. No. 612

SAINT LOUIS, King of France
Relief portrait by Jean de Marco.
Location: House Chamber, above gallery doors.

Neg. No. 613

286

Neg. No. 614

Neg. No. 615

SOLON
Relief portrait by Brenda Putnam.
Location: House Chamber, above gallery doors.

SULEIMAN, Sultan of Turkey
Relief portrait by Joseph Kiselewski.
Location: House Chamber, above gallery doors.

TRIBONIAN
Relief portrait by Brenda Putman.
Location: House Chamber, above gallery doors.

Neg. No. 616

Sculptured Reliefs

STATE SEALS—HOUSE OF REPRESENTATIVES

Upon the completion of the skylight of the Chamber of the House of Representatives in the 1850's a number of the seals of the States and Possessions of the United States were installed in stained glass during 1857–1858. These early seals were painted by Johannes Adam Oertel and others. Additional seals were added as States were admitted to the Union.

During the first construction stage of the remodeling of the House Chamber, 1949, the old cast iron and glass skylight ceiling was removed. In the center of the stainless steel portion of the new ceiling, there is a laylight, the field of which is of carved glass and bronze, outlining the figure of an eagle, illuminated from above. The stained glass seals which had been removed were returned to the various States.

The section between the gallery ceiling and the fretwork surrounding the plaster cove is embellished with painted plaster reproductions of the State Seals formerly painted on glass in the old skylight ceiling removed from the Chamber. The plaster seals are exact reproductions of the old glass seals, both as to design and color. Hawaii and Alaska were the last to be added in 1962.

Diagrammatic Plan of Reflected ceiling of House of Representatives Chamber, 2d (Principal) floor, House Wing, Showing Arrangement of State Seals.

Neg. No. 26072

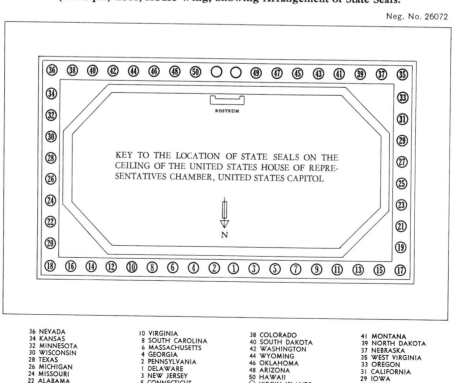

36 NEVADA	10 VIRGINIA	38 COLORADO	41 MONTANA
34 KANSAS	8 SOUTH CAROLINA	40 SOUTH DAKOTA	39 NORTH DAKOTA
32 MINNESOTA	6 MASSACHUSETTS	42 WASHINGTON	37 NEBRASKA
30 WISCONSIN	4 GEORGIA	44 WYOMING	35 WEST VIRGINIA
28 TEXAS	2 PENNSYLVANIA	46 OKLAHOMA	33 OREGON
26 MICHIGAN	1 DELAWARE	48 ARIZONA	31 CALIFORNIA
24 MISSOURI	3 NEW JERSEY	50 HAWAII	29 IOWA
22 ALABAMA	5 CONNECTICUT	O VIRGIN ISLANDS	27 FLORIDA
20 MISSISSIPPI	7 MARYLAND	O PUERTO RICO	25 ARKANSAS
18 LOUISIANA	9 NEW HAMPSHIRE	49 ALASKA	23 MAINE
16 TENNESSEE	11 NEW YORK	47 NEW MEXICO	21 ILLINOIS
14 VERMONT	13 RHODE ISLAND	45 UTAH	19 INDIANA
12 NORTH CAROLINA	15 KENTUCKY	43 IDAHO	17 OHIO

JUSTICE

Sculptured Relief Located in the Old Supreme Court Chamber, First Floor.

This room, S–141, was occupied as the Senate Chamber from 1800 to 1808, and as the Supreme Court Chamber from 1810 to 1860. It was occupied by the Law Library from 1860 to November 1950 and by the Joint Committee on Atomic Energy from 1951 to 1961. It is, therefore, one of the most historic rooms in the Capitol.

The relief, Justice, on the west wall of the room, is attributed to Carlo Franzoni, circa 1817.

In the center of the lunette is a seated, mythical figure of Justice. In her left hand she holds the scales, her right hand resting upon a sword. On the right is an Eagle guarding the Laws; on the left, a youthful winged figure—presumably typifying the Young Nation—crowned by the rising sun, is pointing to the Constitution of the United States.

JUSTICE
Sculptured Relief attributed to Carlo Franzoni.
Location: Old Supreme Court Chamber, first floor.
Neg. No. 13077–A

289

RELIEFS IN THE ROTUNDA, UNITED STATES CAPITOL

WILLIAM PENN'S TREATY WITH THE INDIANS, by Nicholas Gevelot; executed in 1826–1827; located over the north door.

LANDING OF THE PILGRIMS, by Enrico Causici; executed in 1825; located over the east door.

CONFLICT OF DANIEL BOONE AND THE INDIANS, by Enrico Causici; executed in 1826–1827; located over the south door.

THE PRESERVATION OF CAPTAIN SMITH BY POCAHONTAS, by Antonio Capellano; executed circa 1825; located over the west door.

Neg. No. 24560

CONFLICT OF DANIEL BOONE AND THE INDIANS
Relief by Enrico Causici.
Location: over the south door of the Rotunda.

Neg. No. 24561

WILLIAM PENN'S TREATY WITH THE INDIANS
Relief by Nicholas Gevelot.
Location: over the north door of the Rotunda.

290

LANDING OF THE PILGRIMS
Relief by Enrico Causici.
Location: over the east door of the Rotunda.

THE PRESERVATION OF CAPTAIN SMITH BY POCAHONTAS
Relief by Antonio Capellano.
Location: over the west door of the Rotunda.

SCULPTURED PORTRAITS LOCATED IN THE ROTUNDA, UNITED STATES CAPITOL

The sculptured portrait-busts and wreaths on the Rotunda walls were executed by Enrico Causici and Antonio Capellano in 1824. The sculptured portraits portray:

CHRISTOPHER COLUMBUS, located above the painting, "Surrender of General Burgoyne."

SIR WALTER RALEIGH, located above the painting, "Surrender of Lord Cornwallis."

JOHN CABOT, located above the painting, "Landing of Columbus."

RENÉ ROBERT CAVELIER SIEUR DE LA SALLE, located above the painting, "Discovery of the Mississippi River."

Neg. No. 24566

JOHN CABOT, sculptured portrait bust
Relief by Enrico Causici and Antonio Capellano.
Location: above the painting, "Landing of Columbus" in the Rotunda.

CHRISTOPHER COLUMBUS, sculptured portrait bust
Relief by Enrico Causici and Antonio Capellano.
Location: above the painting, "Surrender of General Burgoyne" in the Rotunda.

Neg. No. 24565

Neg. No. 24563

RENÉ ROBERT CAVELIER SIEUR DE LA SALLE, sculptured portrait bust
Relief by Enrico Causici and Antonio Capellano.
Location: above the painting, "Discovery of the Mississippi River" in the Rotunda.

SIR WALTER RALEIGH, sculptured portrait bust
Relief by Enrico Causici and Antonio Capellano.
Location: above the painting, "Surrender of Lord Cornwallis" in the Rotunda.

Neg. No. 24564

294

SCULPTURED PANELS OVER DOORS OF SENATE CHAMBER

These panels by Lee Lawrie, sculptor, were placed when the Senate Chamber was remodeled, 1949–1950.

West entry, "COURAGE," Bruno Mankowski, carver

Courage symbolizes our Nation, which unflinchingly battles Evil and vanquishes it. The biblical symbol for Evil, the serpent, was used.

East entry, "PATRIOTISM," Louis Milione, carver

Patriotism shows a typical citizen leaning on his plow, a symbol of every man's usual work, which he leaves to take up the sword for the defense of his country. The strident eagle symbolizes vigilance and preparedness.

South entry, "WISDOM," Edward H. Ratti, carver

Wisdom is represented by the figure of a woman, from whose head come rays of light. She holds a book symbolizing the experience of the ages, or the Laws. In the other hand she holds a torch which illuminates the sphere representing the earth. The tower on the left is her temple. The stars, earth and clouds suggest that Wisdom is above earthly derivation.

The plaster models of these sculptured panels are located on the walls of the Capitol Terminal of the Senate Subway.

Neg. No. 24722

COURAGE
Sculptured panel by Lee Lawrie, sculptor; carved by Bruno Mankowski.
Location: above doors of Senate Chamber, West entry.

Neg. No. 24720

PATRIOTISM
Sculptured panel by Lee Lawrie, sculptor; carved by Louis Milione.
Location: above doors of Senate Chamber, East entry.

Neg. No. 24721

WISDOM
Sculptured panel by Lee Lawrie, sculptor; carved by Edward H. Ratti.
Location: above doors of Senate Chamber, South entry.

296

EXTERIOR SCULPTURED RELIEFS ON THE EAST FRONT PORTICO

Decorative Wreath Panels

Directly over the niches containing the statues of War and Peace on the East Front Portico, are two panels in relief. In each panel, 13 grouped arrows, symbolic of the 13 original States, are embraced by leafed branches and fruit from the oak and pineapple.

The original sandstone panels were carved by Thomas McIntosh and Jeremiah Sullivan about 1825, according to the best known records. Under the supervision of Paul Manship, both were reproduced in marble during the Extension of the Capitol Project in 1959–1960. G. Giannetti executed the plaster models and the carvers of the Vermont Marble Company carved the reproductions.

The plaster model of one of the decorative wreath panels is located on the East wall in the Senate Subway Terminal, New Senate Office Building. The original sandstone panel is in storage.

Neg. No. 19159

DECORATIVE WREATH PANELS (plaster model)—(2)
Reliefs reproduced in marble from the original sandstone under the supervision of Paul Manship during the Extension of the Capitol Project in 1959–1960. G. Giannetti executed the plaster models and the carvers of the Vermont Marble Company carved the reproductions.
Location: over the niches on the East Front Portico.

Fame and Peace

Above the Rotunda bronze doors of the East Portico is the relief, "Fame and Peace Crowning Washington." The two winged figures, hovering in the air, crown the bust of George Washington with laurel wreaths. Fame, on the right, holds a trumpet, and Peace, on the left, a palm branch.

The original sandstone panel and bust were executed by Antonio Capellano in 1827. Under the supervision of Paul Manship, both were reproduced in marble during the Extension of the Capitol Project in 1959–1960. G. Giannetti executed the plaster models and the carvers of the Vermont Marble Company carved the reproductions.

The plaster model is located on the North wall of the Senate Subway Terminal, New Senate Office Building. The original sandstone panel has been placed in storage.

Neg. No. 20418

FAME AND PEACE CROWNING GEORGE WASHINGTON
Relief and bust—original sandstone by Antonio Capellano.
Plaster model executed by G. Giannetti and carved in marble by the carvers of the Vermont Marble Company all under the supervision of Paul Manship.
Location: above the Rotunda Bronze Door, East Central Portico.

Frescoes and Murals

CANOPY OF THE DOME

(ROTUNDA)

This fresco is entitled, "The Apotheosis of George Washington," and was executed by Constantino Brumidi.

The central figure is that of GEORGE WASHINGTON. On his right is the GODDESS OF LIBERTY, and on his left an idealized figure representing VICTORY and FAME. Surrounding Washington are 13 Maidens, symbolizing the 13 ORIGINAL STATES, with a banner emblazoned with the motto, "E Pluribus Unum."

Six allegorical groupings border all the principal figures. Below Washington is WAR, with Freedom as the central figure. Continuing clockwise, the next group is ARTS AND SCIENCES, with Minerva; MARINE with Neptune; COMMERCE with Mercury; MECHANICS with Vulcan; and, AGRICULTURE with Ceres.

This fresco is the focal point of the great Rotunda. The distance from the floor of the Rotunda to the apex of the painting is 180 feet. The figures, which appear life size, are approximately 15 feet in height. The diameter of the fresco is 62 feet 2 inches, with a concavity of 20 feet 7 inches, containing 4664 superficial feet. The signature of Brumidi appears on this fresco.

The cartoons or sketches were commenced in 1863 and the actual fresco started in 1865 was completed in 1866, about one year's time.

APOTHEOSIS OF WASHINGTON
Fresco by Constantino Brumidi.
Location: Canopy of the Dome.

Neg. No. 14431

THE ROTUNDA FRIEZE

The frieze encircling the Rotunda is located 58 feet above the floor of the Rotunda. It is 300 feet in circumference and 8 feet 3 inches in height. At the bottom of the frieze there is an outward projection of 1 foot. The Rotunda at this point is of brick construction with a plaster finish, and the work heretofore done in fresco upon this frieze has been done in the wet plaster.

Fresco painting is a very ancient method of painting, first used perhaps by the Egyptians. It is a very difficult method, being done by mixing the paint into the wet plaster. This method of painting has been used by the great masters, including Michelangelo. It is referred to by Merrifield as "the most certain and the most durable of all methods and by age it continually acquires beauty and harmony in an infinitely greater degree than any of the others."

Although the work of embellishing the frieze in fresco was commenced by Constantino Brumidi and continued by Filippo Costaggini, all of the work done by these two artists was executed from designs by Brumidi.

The work in fresco upon this frieze was commenced by Brumidi in 1877 and continued by him until his death in 1880. The following subjects, covering about one-third of the embellished frieze, are represented in the panels painted by him:

> Landing of Columbus, 1492.
> Entry of Cortez into the Halls of the Montezumas, 1521.
> Pizarro's Conquest of Peru, 1533.
> Midnight Burial of De Soto in the Mississippi, 1541.
> Pocahontas Saving the Life of Capt. John Smith, 1607.
> Landing of the Pilgrims at Plymouth, Mass., 1620.
> Penn's Treaty With the Indians, 1682. (Approximately Half.)

Following the death of Brumidi, the work of decorating the Rotunda frieze in fresco was continued by Costaggini during the period 1880–88.

The following subjects, covering about two-thirds of the embellished frieze, are represented in the panels painted by him (including half of the Penn panel):

> Settlement of the Plymouth Colony, 1620.
> Peace Between Governor Oglethorpe and the Indians, 1732.
> Battle of Lexington, 1775.
> Reading of the Declaration of Independence, 1776.
> Surrender of Cornwallis at Yorktown, 1781.
> The Death of Tecumseh at the Battle of Thames, 1813.
> Entry of General Scott into the City of Mexico, 1847.
> Discovery of Gold in California, 1848.

At this point 270 feet had been accomplished. As no designs were agreed upon or approved for the remainder of the frieze prior to the death of Costaggini in 1904, there had been a 30-foot gap for some 65 years, until recently.

Numerous efforts through legislation to complete the frieze were unsuccessful until the 81st Congress, when the Jenkins resolution was signed into law. Originally it was Representative Jenkins' intention to honor exclusively the Wright brothers and their creation of powered flight, but the Joint Committee on the Library, under the chairmanship of Senator Theodore Francis Green, amended the resolution to include therein the two great conflicts of that era, and in this form the measure was adopted. Under its terms the Joint Committee on the Library engaged Allyn Cox, a distinguished New York artist skilled in fresco painting, to embellish the final three panels. The joint resolution directed that they represent (1) the Civil War, (2) the Spanish-American War, and (3) the birth of aviation in the United States. Mr. Cox completed these panels in the summer of 1953, and cleaned and restored the original portion in the fall. Thus the cycle of great events in American History carries us from the wind-driven sailing craft of Columbus to the spectacular air age of the twentieth century Wright brothers.

Original Sketches of the Rotunda Frieze

Original sketches of the Rotunda Frieze, by Constantino Brumidi were presented to the government by Mrs. Myrtle Cheney Murdock in 1961; located in the Architect's Office, Room SB–14.

Historical Events depicted in the Frieze of the Rotunda of the United States Capitol.

The Landing of Columbus in the New World, 1492.

Cortez Enters The Halls of Montezuma, 1521.

Conquest of Peru by Pizarro, 1533.

Midnight Burial of De Soto in the Mississippi, 1541.

Pocahontas Saves the Life of Capt. John Smith, 1606.

Landing of the Pilgrims at Plymouth, Mass., 1620.

Settlement of Plymouth Colony, 1620.

Penn's Treaty With the Indians, 1682.

Oglethorpe's Treaty with the Indians, 1732.

The Battle of Lexington, 1775.

Reading of the Declaration of Independence, 1776.

Surrender of Cornwallis at Yorktown, 1781.

Death of Tecumseh at the Battle of the Thames, 1813.

Entry of Gen. Scott into the City of Mexico, 1847.

Discovery of Gold in California, 1848.

The Civil War, 1865.

The Spanish-American War, 1898.

Birth of Aviation in the United States, 1903.

SENATE WING, FRESCOES AND MURALS

(By Constantino Brumidi and assistants and other artists)

SENATE APPROPRIATIONS COMMITTEE ROOMS. Decorations by Constantino Brumidi.

Lunettes, Wall Frescoes, Room S–128, the former Senate Military Affairs Committee Room. (Several commenced 1858; all completed by 1871.)

> Boston Massacre, 1770 (North Wall)
> Battle of Lexington, 1775 (South Wall)
> Death of General Wooster, 1777 (North Wall)
> Washington at Valley Forge, 1778 (South Wall)
> Storming of Stony Point, 1779 (East Wall)

Panels of walls and pilasters represent arms and armor of different periods, nations and races, ancient and modern. The pilasters were painted by James Leslie.

Medallion Head of Liberty, surrounded by flags and weapons of war—on West Wall.

Ceiling is frescoed with victors' wreaths, shields and other emblems of war.

Allegorical groupings, Room S–127. Decorated for the room as occupied by the Committee on Naval Affairs.

> Maidens of the Navy
> Marine Gods and Goddesses
> Indian Heads
> Ancient Porticoes and Antique Vessels.

Neg. No. 26194

THE BATTLE OF LEXINGTON, 1775
Lunette by Constantino Brumidi.
Location: South wall of the Senate Appropriations Committee Room, S–128.

THE BOSTON MASSACRE, 1770
Lunette by Constantino Brumidi.
Location: North wall of the Senate Appropriations Committee Room, S–128.

DEATH OF GENERAL WOOSTER, 1777
Lunette by Constantino Brumidi.
Location: North wall of the Senate Appropriations Committee Room, S–128.

STORMING OF STONY POINT, 1779
Lunette by Constantino Brumidi.
Location: East wall of the Senate Appropriations Committee Room, S–128.

WASHINGTON AT VALLEY FORGE, 1778
Lunette by Constantino Brumidi.
Location: South wall of the Senate Appropriations Committee Room, S–128.

SENATE APPROPRIATONS COMMITTEE ROOM, S–129. Decorations by Carl Rakeman were executed 1909.

Portraits of Generals of the Revolutionary period in lunettes: (No illustrations.)

> George Washington (East wall)
> Joseph Warren (South wall)
> Anthony Wayne (West wall)
> Horatio Gates (North wall)

DEMOCRATIC POLICY COMMITTEE ROOM, S–118, the former Senate Foreign Relations Committee Room. Decorations by Constantino Brumidi.

Profiles of former Senate Foreign Relations Committee Chairmen, executed about 1874. (No illustrations.)

> Henry Clay, Chairman, 1834–1836 (North wall)
> Simon E. Cameron, Chairman, 1871–1877 (East wall)
> William Allen, Chairman, 1845–1846 (South wall)
> Charles W. Sumner, Chairman, 1861–1871 (West wall)

The ceiling is decorated with four black eagles in distemper. (Artist unknown.)

PRESIDENT'S ROOM, S–216. Frescoes and oil paintings by Constantino Brumidi, execution begun about 1859–1860.

Portrait of George Washington.

Portraits of the Members of Washington's first cabinet (Walls)

> Thomas Jefferson—Secretary of State
> Alexander Hamilton—Secretary of the Treasury
> Henry Knox—Secretary of War
> Edmund Randolph—Attorney General
> Samuel Osgood—Postmaster General

Symbolic portraits (Ceiling)

> William Brewster—Religion
> Christopher Columbus—Discovery
> Benjamin Franklin—History
> Americus Vespucius—Exploration

Symbolic Madonna figures (Ceiling) (No illustrations.)

> Religion
> Legislation
> Liberty
> Executive Authority

Neg. No. 26220
WALL PANEL representing arms and armor of different periods, nations and races, ancient and modern
Panel designed by Constantino Brumidi; painted by James Leslie.
Location: wall of Senate Appropriations Committee Room, S–128.

305

WILLIAM BREWSTER, symbolic portrait depicting Religion
Mural (portrait) by Constantino Brumidi.
Location: Ceiling of President's Room, Senate wing.

CHRISTOPHER COLUMBUS, symbolic portrait depicting Discovery
Mural (portrait) by Constantino Brumidi.
Location: ceiling of President's Room, Senate wing.

307

BENJAMIN FRANKLIN, symbolic portrait depicting History
Mural (portrait) by Constantino Brumidi.
Location: ceiling of President's Room, Senate wing.

ALEXANDER HAMILTON, Secretary of the Treasury
Mural (medallion portrait) by Constantino Brumidi.
Location: wall of President's Room, Senate wing.

THOMAS JEFFERSON, Secretary of State
Mural (medallion portrait) by Constantino Brumidi.
Location: wall of President's Room, Senate wing.

310

HENRY KNOX, Secretary of War
Mural (medallion portrait) by Constantino Brumidi.
Location: wall of President's Room, Senate wing.

311

SAMUEL OSGOOD, Postmaster General
Mural (medallion portrait) by Constantino Brumidi.
Location: wall of President's Room, Senate wing.

Neg. No. 25908

EDMUND RANDOLPH, Attorney General
Mural (medallion portrait) by Constantino Brumidi.
Location: wall of President's Room, Senate wing.

313

AMERICUS VESPUCIUS, symbolic portrait depicting Exploration
Mural (portrait) by Constantino Brumidi.
Location: ceiling of President's Room, Senate wing.

314

Neg. No. 26560

GEORGE WASHINGTON
Portrait by Constantino Brumidi.
Location: south wall of President's Room, S–216, second floor.

315

FORMER OFFICE OF THE VICE PRESIDENT, earlier the District of Columbia Committee Rooms, S–211 and S–212. Decorations by Constantino Brumidi. (No illustrations)

Allegorical groupings, (Ceiling Murals), Room S–211, decorated originally for the Senate Library, executed from 1858 through 1867.

 Physics
 History
 Telegraph
 Geography
 Three Graces (4 groups)

Allegorical designs, Room S–212, at one time the Office of the Sergeant at Arms.

Wall Frescoes:
 Secession and Products of North and South
 War and Strife
 Rods United—"E Pluribus Unum"
 Implements of War Destroyed

Ceiling Fresco:
 Columbia Welcoming the South Back into the Union (signed Brumidi 1876)

SENATE RECEPTION ROOM, S–213. Decorations by Constantino Brumidi. (No illustrations.)

Mural on South wall:
 George Washington in Consultation with Thomas Jefferson and Alexander Hamilton, (embellished in 1870–1873).

Allegorical groupings—Ceiling. Executed in 1871 and 1872.

Circular Arch—South

 La Jurisprudence (Jurisprudence)—Southeast
 La Force (Strength or Power)—Northwest
 La Sapience (Wisdom)—Northeast
 La Prudence (Discretion)—Southwest

Groined Arch—North

 La Guerre (War)—West
 La Paix (Peace)—East
 Les Sciences (Sciences) (Liberty)—North
 Les Arts de l'Industrie (Industrial Arts)—South

MAIN CORRIDOR, first floor. Decorations by Constantino Brumidi.

Medallion portraits: (Mural monochromes)
 Andrew Jackson (Illustration)
 Henry Clay (Illustration)
 Daniel Webster
 ——— Adams

Large portraits:
 Justice Joseph Story
 Chancellor Kent

Represented as sculpture: (bust)
 Chancellor Robert R. Livingston, executed 1878.

14 oval landscapes in oil (walls and ceiling).

Mural monochrome portrait of ANDREW JACKSON
Portrait by Constantino Brumidi.
Located in the Senate wing, first floor corridor.

Neg. No. 23678

Mural monochrome portrait of HENRY CLAY
Portrait by Constantino Brumidi.
Located in the Senate wing, first floor corridor.

Neg. No. 24261

NORTH CORRIDOR—extending East and West, first floor. Decorations by Constantino Brumidi.

Medallion portraits: (Mural monochromes)

Thomas Jefferson
Richard Montgomery
Silas Deane
Horatio Gates
Daniel Morgan

Benjamin Franklin
Joseph Warren
Thomas Mifflin
Israel Putnam
Jonathan Trumbull

Frescoes: (Large murals)

Signing of the First Treaty of Peace with Great Britain, 1782. Executed in 1874 after a sketch by Benjamin West. (No illustration.)

Cession of Louisiana (Negotiation for the Acquisition of Louisiana) executed 1875.

Neg. No. 23672

Mural monochrame portrait of SILAS DEANE
Portrait by Constantino Brumidi.
Located in the Senate wing, first floor corridor.

Neg. No. 23677

Mural monochrome portrait of BENJAMIN FRANKLIN
Portrait by Constantino Brumidi.
Located in the Senate wing, first floor corridor.

Mural monochrome portrait of HORATIO GATES
Portrait by Constantino Brumidi.
Located in the Senate wing, first floor corridor.

Neg. No. 23673

Mural monochrome portrait of THOMAS JEFFERSON
Portrait by Constantino Brumidi.
Located in the Senate wing, first floor corridor.

Neg. No. 23680

Neg. No. 23682

Mural monochrome portrait of THOMAS MIFFLIN
Portrait by Constantino Brumidi.
Located in the Senate wing, first floor corridor.

Neg. No. 23683

Mural monochrome portrait of RICHARD
MONTGOMERY
Portrait by Constantino Brumidi.
Located in the Senate wing, first floor corridor.

Mural monochrome portrait of DANIEL MORGAN
Portrait by Constantino Brumidi.
Located in the Senate wing, first floor corridor.

Neg. No. 23684

Mural monochrome portrait of ISRAEL PUTNAM
Portrait by Constantino Brumidi.
Located in the Senate wing, first floor corridor.

Neg. No. 23674

318

Neg. No. 23688

Mural monochrome portrait of JONATHAN
TRUMBULL
Portrait by Constantino Brumidi.
Located in the Senate wing, first floor corridor.

Neg. No. 23689

Mural monochrome portrait of JOSEPH WARREN
Portrait by Constantino Brumidi.
Located in the Senate wing, first floor corridor.

Neg. No. 10678

CESSION OF LOUISIANA (Negotiation for the Acquisition of Louisiana)
Fresco by Constantino Brumidi.
Location: Senate wing, first floor, north corridor.

319

SOUTH CORRIDOR, first floor. Decorations by Constantino Brumidi. (No illustration.)

8 studies in oil (animals).

8 ovals in oil (United States shields).

WEST CORRIDOR—extending North and South, first floor. Decorations by Constantino Brumidi.

Medallion portraits: (Mural monochromes)

Robert R. Livingston
John Jay
Charles Carroll of Carrollton
John Hancock
Francis Hopkinson

Roger Sherman
Charles Thomson
Robert Morris

Frescoes: (Large murals)

Bartolome de Las Casas, the Apostle of the Indians. (No illustration.)

Bellona, the Roman Goddess of War (executed 1875). (No illustration.)

Columbus and the Indian Maiden

Authority Consults the Written Law

13 oval landscapes in oil (walls and ceiling). (No illustration.)

12 Signs of the Zodiac (ceiling). (No illustration.)

Neg. No. 23671

Mural monochrome portrait of CHARLES CARROLL
Portrait by Constantino Brumidi.
Located in the Senate wing, first floor corridor.

Neg. No. 23675

Mural monochrome portrait of JOHN HANCOCK
Portrait by Constantino Brumidi.
Located in the Senate wing, first floor corridor.

Mural monochrome portrait of FRANCIS HOPKINSON
Portrait by Constantino Brumidi.
Located in the Senate wing, first floor corridor.

Neg. No. 23676

Mural monochrome portrait of JOHN JAY
Portrait by Constantino Brumidi.
Located in the Senate wing, first floor corridor.

Neg. No. 23679

Neg. No. 23681

Mural monochrome portrait of ROBERT R.
LIVINGSTON
Portrait by Constantino Brumidi.
Located in the Senate wing, first floor corridor.

Neg. No. 23685

Mural monochrome portrait of ROBERT MORRIS
Portrait by Constantino Brumidi.
Located in the Senate wing, first floor corridor.

Mural monochrome portrait of ROGER SHERMAN
Portrait by Constantino Brumidi.
Located in the Senate wing, first floor corridor.
Neg. No. 23686

Mural monochrome portrait of CHARLES THOMSON
Portrait by Constantino Brumidi.
Located in the Senate wing, first floor corridor.
Neg. No. 23687

COLUMBUS and the INDIAN MAIDEN
Mural by Constantino Brumidi.
Location: West corridor, first floor, Senate wing.

AUTHORITY CONSULTS the WRITTEN LAW
Mural by Constantino Brumidi.
Location: West corridor, first floor, Senate wing.

PATENT CORRIDOR, First floor, east end of north corridor.

When Constantino Brumidi decorated this corridor in 1873, the Committee on Patents occupied a room facing it; those depicted were inventors and the ceiling was decorated with representations of modern inventions.

Murals:

Robert Fulton, with his steamboat, the Clermont, the Palisades of the Hudson and an easel showing a portrait of De Witt Clinton.

John Fitch, working on his model of a steamboat.   (Illustration.)

Benjamin Franklin, shown in his laboratory.

Neg. No. 26684

JOHN FITCH
Mural by Constantino Brumidi.
Location: Patent corridor, first floor, east end of north corridor, Senate wing.

HOUSE WING

HOUSE COMMITTEE ON APPROPRIATIONS ROOM, H–143, the former House
Committee on Insular Affairs.   The decorations by Henry Lyman Sayen, executed
1903–1905, are illustrative of past conditions in the insular possessions of the
United States.

Lunettes cemented to the walls:

Rule of Tyranny (No illustration)
Rule of Justice or Peace (No illustration)
Primitive Agriculture
Good Government

Neg. No. 26683

GOOD GOVERNMENT
Lunette by Henry Lyman Sayen.
Location: House Appropriations Committee Room, H–143.

Neg. No. 26682

PRIMITIVE AGRICULTURE
Lunette by Henry Lyman Sayen.
Location: House Appropriations Committee Room, H–143.

324

HOUSE APPROPRIATIONS COMMITTEE ROOM, H–144, the former Agriculture Committee Room. Decorations by Constantino Brumidi. Executed in 1855–1856. First fresco decorations in the United States Capitol. Frescoes:

Murals
Calling of Cincinnatus from the Plow
Calling of Putnam from the Plow to the Revolution

Wall scenes in oil
Cutting Grain with a Sickle
Harvesting Grain with a McCormick Reaper

Medallion heads:
George Washington
Thomas Jefferson

Ceiling fresco groups:

Spring	Autumn
Summer	Winter

Neg. No. 26671

CALLING of CINCINNATUS from the PLOW
Fresco by Constantino Brumidi.
Location: House Appropriations Committee Room, H–144.

Neg. No. 26670

CALLING of PUTNAM from the PLOW to the REVOLUTION
Fresco by Constantino Brumidi.
Location: House Appropriations Committee Room, H–144.

Medallion head of THOMAS JEFFERSON and HARVESTING GRAIN with a McCORMICK REAPER

Wall scene in oil by Constantino Brumidi.

Location: House Appropriations Committee Room, H–144.

Medallion head of GEORGE WASHINGTON and CUTTING GRAIN with a SICKLE
Wall scene in oil by Constantino Brumidi.
Location: House Appropriations Committee Room, H-144.

AUTUMN
Ceiling fresco group by Constantino Brumidi.
Location: House Appropriations Committee Room, H–144.

328

SPRING
Ceiling fresco group by Constantino Brumidi.
Location: House Appropriations Committee Room, H–144.

SUMMER
Ceiling fresco group by Constantino Brumidi.
Location: House Appropriations Committee Room, H–144.

Neg. No. 26665

330

WINTER
Ceiling fresco group by Constantino Brumidi.
Location: House Appropriations Committee Room, H–144.

"CORNWALLIS SUES FOR CESSATION OF HOSTILITIES UNDER THE FLAG OF TRUCE," fresco, executed by Constantino Brumidi in 1857. The mural was formerly on the south wall of the Hall of the House of Representatives; in 1950 it was covered when the House Chamber was remodeled; it was uncovered, prepared and moved to its present location in the Members' Private Dining Room, H–130, in December 1961. The Consolidated Engineering Company of Baltimore, Maryland was responsible for the removal of the fresco. The work was supervised and directed by a conservator of paintings, Henri G. Courtais, at which time it was restored by the artist, Allyn Cox.

The fresco represents a scene at the headquarters of General Washington at Yorktown on October 17, 1781. Washington is depicted standing, in the act of receiving the letter from the emissary sent by Lord Cornwallis through the battle lines under the flag of truce. The British general requested a 24 hour cessation of hostilities while the terms of surrender might be considered, but Washington, fearing the arrival of the British fleet, gave only a 2 hour cease-fire order. Cornwallis was thus forced into the final surrender which occurred on October 19, 1781. Lord Cornwallis was not present at either of these historic events. On the strap of the brief case, lower right, is the signature, "C. Brumidi artist. Citizen of the U.S."

Neg. No. 22180

CORNWALLIS SUES FOR CESSATION OF HOSTILITIES UNDER THE FLAG OF TRUCE
Fresco by Constantino Brumidi.
Location: Members' Private Dining Room, House wing, first floor.

Miscellaneous Works of Art in the United States Capitol (*Interior*)

MANTELS IN THE UNITED STATES CAPITOL

When Charles Bulfinch became the third Architect of the Capitol in 1818, the reconstruction of the original North and South wings of the Capitol, which had been destroyed in 1814, was well under way according to the designs of Benjamin Henry Latrobe. The work had progressed so far, in fact, that Bulfinch had no alternative but to carry on the work as designed by his predecessor. Among the items he inherited were fifty marble mantels.

Some of these mantels are still in existence, and those remaining in the Capitol are among the finest examples of mantel design during the Federal Period to be found in America. The fact that so many still remain in the Capitol is particularly interesting when one considers the alterations and additions, the fires and explosions and the changes in heating methods which have occurred in the Capitol since the time of Bulfinch and Latrobe. Notable among these are the finely carved marble mantels in the Old Senate Chamber on the Second Floor, a room later used by the Supreme Court.

These four mantels, executed from a drawing by Giovanni Andrei at the direction of Latrobe, were ordered from James Traquair in Philadelphia about 1812. Because of war time shipping dangers they had not been sent to Washington, so at the time of the British destruction in 1814, they were saved by their absence. When the Capitol was rebuilt, these mantels, having been crated and boxed for three years, were available. Traquair and Co. was paid $800 for them in 1817.

During the rebuilding, six mantels were obtained from James Hodge of Albany, New York, and at least four others were purchased from the Milford Marble Co. of New Haven, Conn. The identity and location of these mantels is not known.

By the time Thomas U. Walter became Architect of the Capitol in 1851, and the building of the present Senate and House wings had begun, styles had changed. The slender reeding and vertical lines of the Federal Period had given way to the curving opulence of the Victorian, and these new styles were incorporated into the mantels of the new wings. At the same time some occupants of the older central part of the building, wishing to be more in keeping with the times, had their earlier mantels removed and replaced with the new styles which had semi-circular openings and, in some cases, grates for the burning of coal.

In addition, several mantels of this later design may be found on the various floors of the West Central Wing. This is the area formerly occupied by the Library of Congress and rebuilt after a fire destroyed the Library in 1851. The Library moved to its new building in 1897, afterwhich this area was reconstructed for offices in 1900.

In carrying out the work on the recently completed East Central Front Extension, the mantels of the Old Senate Chamber were used as the basis for the design of the new mantels in the Senate Conference Room and House Reception Room in the Connecting wings on the Second Floor.

Photographs show some of the fine old mantels referred to above which are still in the Capitol, as well as the newly completed mantels in the East Front Extension.

Neg. No. 25295

MANTEL
Location: Room H–164, first floor, House wing.

Neg. No. 25294

MANTEL
Location: Room H–163, first floor, House wing.

Neg. No. 25082

MANTEL
Location: Room H–157, first floor, House wing.

Neg. No. 24892

MANTEL
Location: Room S–150, first floor, Senate wing.

Neg. No. 24893

MANTEL
Location: Room H–162, first floor, House wing.

Neg. No. 24891

MANTEL
Location: Room S–148, first floor, Senate wing.

Neg. No. 24205

MANTEL
Location: Room H–151, first floor, House wing.

Neg. No. 24204

MANTEL
Location: Room H–116, first floor, House wing.

Neg. No. 24202

MANTEL
Location: Room H–110, first floor, House wing.

Neg. No. 24433

MANTEL
Location: Room SB–15, basement floor, Senate wing.

Neg. No. 16906

MANTEL
Location: Room S–228, second floor, Senate wing.

Neg. No. 16904

MANTEL
Location: Room S–228, second floor, Senate wing.

Neg. No. 16905

Neg. No. 24890

MANTEL (one of two identical mantels)
Location: Room S–228, second floor, Senate wing.

MANTEL
Location: Room SB–18, basement floor, Senate wing

MODEL OF THE UNITED STATES CAPITOL

This study model of plaster was constructed by the Office of the Architect of the Capitol in 1903–1904 through the employment of Emile Garet, modeler, with trained assistants, when the Honorable Joseph G. Cannon was Speaker of the House of Representatives, for the purpose of showing the proposed extension of the East Front of the Capitol.

The dimensions are:

Length: 12 feet 7 inches.

Width: 5 feet 9½ inches.

Height: 4 feet 9½ inches (From platform to top of Statue of Freedom).

Platform on which model rests is: 13 feet ½ inch long, 6 feet wide, 4 inches thick.

During the period 1937–1938, the model which had been stored in various spaces in the Capitol Building, was placed for display in the Crypt of the Capitol. Necessary repairs were made and in order to provide proper protection from accident and dust, it was placed on a wood table about which a velvet curtain, weighted at the bottom, was hung, and the model completely enclosed by a glass case. The case is constructed in sections so that it may be readily removed for dismantling for moving or shipment of the model.

The model has been exhibited in several expositions in this country and abroad, including:

1915: Panama Pacific International Exposition, San Francisco, California

1926: Sesquicentennial Exposition, Philadelphia, Pennsylvania

1928–29: International Exposition, Seville, Spain

1937: Great Lakes Exposition, Cleveland, Ohio.

At the Exposition at Seville, Spain, the Jury of Awards selected the model as the outstanding feature of the exhibit of the Commission of Fine Arts and awarded it the Gold Medal. This distinction is pleasing to those who have seen this wonderful model of the Capitol and admired it for its beauty and its accuracy in the workmanship displayed.

337

MODEL of the United States Capitol
Constructed by Emile Garet and his assistants.
Location: Crypt, first floor, United States Capitol.

MOTTOES IN PLAQUES OR PANELS

(No illustrations)

"In God We Trust"[1]—In 1962 three of the stars in back of the Speaker's rostrum in the House Chamber were removed and this inscription was placed there December 19, 1962 in accordance with House Res. 740, 87th Congress, 2nd session.

"Annuit Coeptis"—(God has favored our undertakings)—over the East entrance doorway, Senate Chamber.

"Novus Ordo Seclorum"—(A new order of the ages is born)—over the West entrance doorway, Senate Chamber.

"In God We Trust"—over the South entrance, Senate Chamber.

"E Pluribus Unum"—(One out of many)—carved in the panel behind the Vice President's rostrum.

[1] See also *Plaques* for "In God We Trust" bronze plaques located in the Longworth House Office Building and the New Senate Office Building.

PLAQUES AND MARKERS

BRONZE MARKER on the floor in Statuary Hall marks the spot where John Quincy Adams, former President of the United States, and at the time of his death a Member of the House of Representatives, fell to the floor mortally ill, Feb. 21, 1848 and died a few days later on February 23d. Marker was placed in 1888. (No illustration.)

PLAQUE commemorating the laying of the cornerstone of the Capitol in 1793; placed during the 1932 Washington Bicentennial Celebration; located in the Old Supreme Court entrance, East Front.

Neg. No. 11681

339

PLAQUE commemorating the 1893 centennial of the laying of the cornerstone of the Capitol in 1793; located on the wall at the Old Supreme Court entrance, East Front, to mark the spot where the original cornerstone was laid.

Neg. No. 24611

PLAQUE
Commemorating the 1893 centennial of the laying of the cornerstone of the Capitol
in 1793.
Location: on the wall at the Old Supreme Court entrance, East Front.

PLAQUE—Declaration of Independence; accepted as a gift of Michael Francis Doyle in 1952; located in the Rotunda.

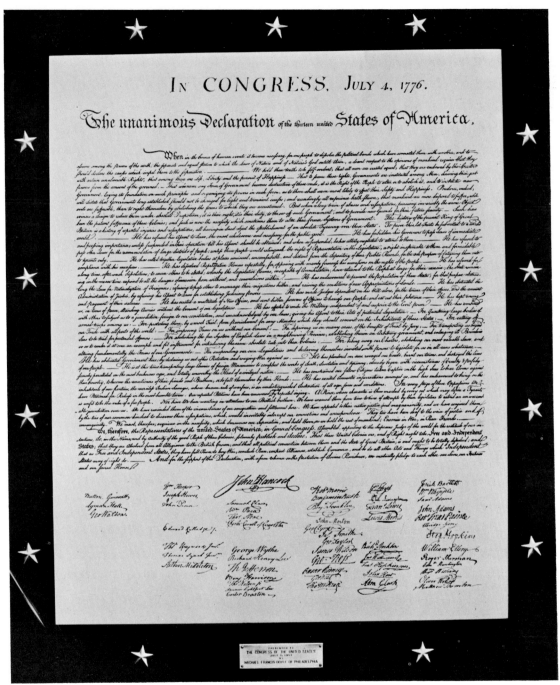

Neg. No. 951

PLAQUE
Declaration of Independence.
Location: Rotunda.

PLAQUE or tablet over the gallery door in back of the Speaker's rostrum in the House Chamber; the inscription is a quotation from Daniel Webster's speech at the laying of the cornerstone of the Bunker Hill Monument at Charlestown, Boston, Massachusetts, on June 17, 1825. This marble tablet was installed during the period of remodeling of the House Chamber, 1949–1950.

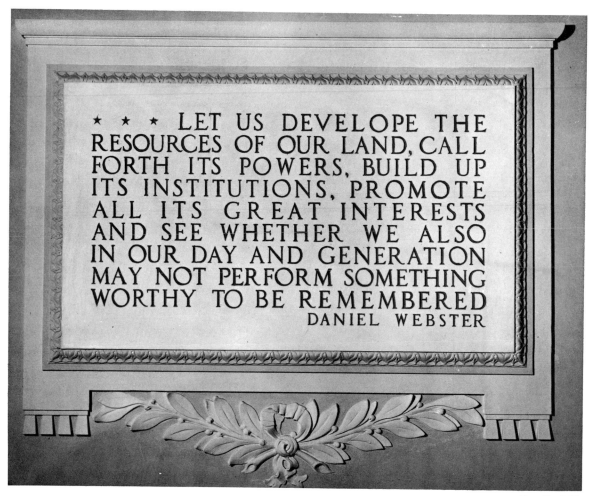

★ ★ ★ LET US DEVELOPE THE RESOURCES OF OUR LAND, CALL FORTH ITS POWERS, BUILD UP ITS INSTITUTIONS, PROMOTE ALL ITS GREAT INTERESTS AND SEE WHETHER WE ALSO IN OUR DAY AND GENERATION MAY NOT PERFORM SOMETHING WORTHY TO BE REMEMBERED
DANIEL WEBSTER

PLAQUE marking the first meeting place of the House of Representatives in the Capitol; located in the Senate wing, outside Senate Disbursing Office, S–233; placed in 1952.

THE FIRST MEETING PLACE
OF THE
HOUSE OF REPRESENTATIVES
IN THE CAPITOL
1800 — 1801
1804 — 1807

THIS TABLET MARKS THE FIRST MEETING PLACE OF THE HOUSE OF REPRESENTATIVES IN THE CAPITOL. HERE — ON NOVEMBER 18, 1800 — THE HOUSE OF REPRESENTATIVES MET FOR THE FIRST TIME IN WASHINGTON, REMAINING THROUGH THE SECOND SESSION OF THE SIXTH CONGRESS. HERE, FROM FEBRUARY 11 TO FEBRUARY 17, 1801, THE HOUSE CAST 36 SUCCESSIVE BALLOTS TO ELECT THOMAS JEFFERSON PRESIDENT OF THE UNITED STATES IN THE CONTEST BETWEEN JEFFERSON AND AARON BURR.

ON NOVEMBER 5, 1804, THE ROOM AGAIN BECAME TEMPORARY QUARTERS OF THE HOUSE OF REPRESENTATIVES — DURING THE SECOND SESSION OF THE EIGHTH CONGRESS AND THE WHOLE OF THE NINTH, ADJOURNED MARCH 3, 1807.

PRESENTED BY
THE NATIONAL CAPITAL SESQUICENTENNIAL COMMISSION
1951

Neg. No. 11620

PLAQUES, bronze (two) inscribed "IN GOD WE TRUST"; one is located in the Main Lobby, East wall, Longworth House Office Building and the other one is in a small niche on the west side of the Southwest entrance to the New Senate Office Building; placed in 1961.

Neg. No. 20486

PLAQUE
Two identical bronze plaques installed in the New Senate Office Building (shown) and the Longworth House Office Building.

PLAQUE, bronze, in the House Reception Room, Capitol Extension, commemorating Sam Rayburn, during whose Speakership the Extension of the Capitol Project was undertaken; placed July 6, 1962.

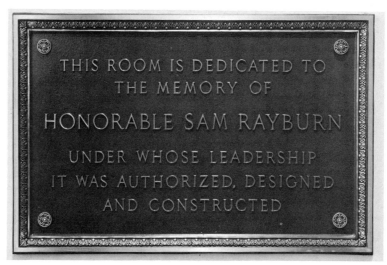

Neg. No. 22664

PLAQUE
Speaker Sam Rayburn.
Location: House Reception Room, House wing, second floor.

PLASTER PLAQUES of the Seals of the States and Possessions of the United States; these replaced the glass Seals which were removed when the House Chamber was remodeled, 1949–1950; located in the ceiling of the House Chamber. (No illustrations.) (The text and diagram on the seals of States and Possessions of the United States is carried under Sculptured Reliefs-State Seals).

PLAQUE marking the first Senate Chamber in the Capitol; located in the Senate wing, first floor; placed in 1952.

THE FIRST SENATE CHAMBER
1800 — 1808

THIS TABLET MARKS THE LOCATION OF THE FIRST SENATE CHAMBER IN THE CAPITOL. HERE, ON NOVEMBER 21, 1800, THE SENATE MET FOR THE FIRST TIME IN WASHINGTON — FOR THE SECOND SESSION OF THE SIXTH CONGRESS. HERE, PRESIDENT JOHN ADAMS, ON NOVEMBER 22, 1800, DELIVERED HIS LAST ANNUAL MESSAGE TO BOTH HOUSES. HERE, THOMAS JEFFERSON, AFTER PRESIDING OVER THE SENATE DURING THE SESSION, TOOK OATH OF OFFICE, ON MARCH 4, 1801, FROM CHIEF JUSTICE JOHN MARSHALL, AS PRESIDENT OF THE UNITED STATES AND DELIVERED HIS FIRST INAUGURAL ADDRESS.

HERE, ON MARCH 4, 1805, PRESIDENT JEFFERSON DELIVERED HIS SECOND INAUGURAL ADDRESS.

HERE THE SENATE CONTINUED TO MEET, PRESIDED OVER BY VICE PRESIDENTS AARON BURR AND GEORGE CLINTON, THROUGH THE FIRST SESSION OF THE TENTH CONGRESS, ADJOURNED APRIL 25, 1808.

PRESENTED BY
THE NATIONAL CAPITAL SESQUICENTENNIAL COMMISSION
1951

Neg. No. 11618

39–071 O—65——24

BRONZE TABLET in the Speaker's Lobby; placed in 1924; designed by Paul Wayland Bartlett, with the text of the inscription by Charles E. Fairman. A tribute to the Speakers of the House whose portraits hang in this lobby.

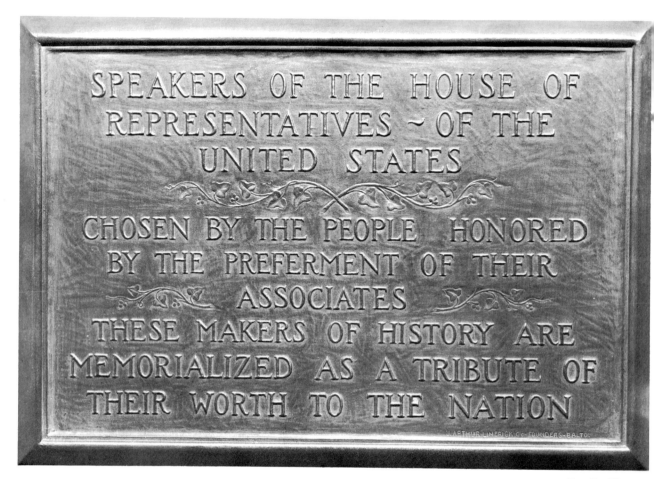

PLAQUE commemorating the centennial of the telegraph to mark the room from which Samuel F. B. Morse sent the message, "What Hath God Wrought!"; located in the small rotunda, Central section, first floor; unveiled May 24, 1944.

PLAQUE—CENTENNIAL OF THE TELEGRAPH
Unveiled: May 24, 1944.
Location: Small rotunda, Central section, first floor.

PLAQUE from the Conrad and McMunn Hotel was removed about 1929 from the site of the Longworth House Office Building. It was from this hotel that Thomas Jefferson walked to the Capitol for his inauguration in 1801. Plaque is located in the Architect's Storeroom.

PLAQUE—Henry Wilson, Vice President of the United States; located in the Vice President's Room, S–214, where Mr. Wilson died, November 22, 1875.

Neg. No. 27251

PLAQUE from the Conrad and McMunn Hotel, site of the Longworth House Office Building
Location: Stored in the Architect's Storeroom.

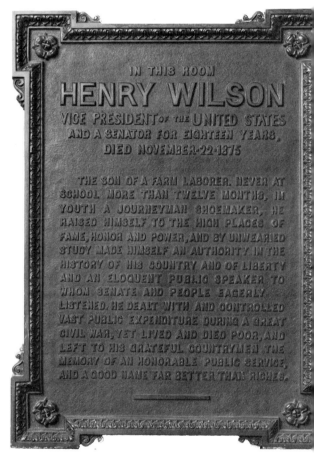

Neg. No. 25809

HENRY WILSON, Vice President of the United States Plaque located in the Vice President's Room, S–214, where Mr. Wilson died November 22, 1875.

PLAQUE marking the lot No. 16 in Square No. 634 on North Capitol Street, acquired by George Washington in 1798, upon which he built two brick dwellings from designs by William Thornton, first Architect of the Capitol. The bronze tablet on a granite base is on the broad walk of the Fountain Terrace (formerly North Capitol Street) and was erected as part of the construction of the Fountain, Terrace and Garage.

PLAQUE marking the dedication of thirty-one trees in one group to the thirty-one Presidents of the Daughters of the American Revolution (1934) by the thirty-one Chapters in Maryland as part of the Tercentenary Celebration of the founding of the State of Maryland. The land on which the trees stand was ceded by the State to the government for the National Capital in 1790. The bronze plaque on a rough granite stone is located on the Union Station Plaza, south of the roadway between Louisiana and Delaware Avenues, N.E., in the enlarged Capitol Grounds.

CENTENNIAL SAFE

This safe was displayed as a feature of the Centennial Exposition in Philadelphia which opened in May 1876. It was the property of Mrs. A. M. (C. F.) Deihm of New York City, publisher of the weekly paper, *Our Second Century*. Mrs. Deihm gave it gratuitously to the Government, with the request that it remain locked for one hundred years.

It was moved from Philadelphia to the United States Capitol in 1877 and placed in Statuary Hall, where it was exhibited. It was closed and locked on February 22, 1879, to be opened on the occasion of the Second Centennial of the Independence of the United States, 1976.

The safe was removed from Statuary Hall in 1879 following legislation approved March 3, 1879 forbidding the exhibition in Statuary Hall, the Rotunda, or the corridors of the Capitol of any work of art or manufacture not the property of the United States. The safe was placed under the Central Portico, East Front of the Capitol, and remained there until December 12, 1958, when it was moved to a space just inside the Crypt on the first floor, while work on the Extension of the Capitol was in progress. At the present time it is in a storage room off the northeast quadrant of the Crypt.

The safe, manufactured by the Marvin Safe Company, is about 50 inches wide, 40 inches deep, and 64 inches high, excluding an ornamental pediment at the top. It is supposed to contain an album of photographs of distinguished men of its period from varied fields of endeavor, a second album of autographs, a silver inkstand and other items.

An illustration of the safe and an article regarding it are to be found in *President James A. Garfield's Memorial Journal* published by C. F. Deihm in 1882. The illustration is interesting historically, but differs in many respects from the actual safe.

Neg. No. 11632

CENTENNIAL SAFE
View of safe used in President James A. Garfield's Memorial Journal.
Location: storage room off northeast quadrant of Crypt.

CENTENNIAL SAFE
Safe manufactured by the Marvin Safe Company.
Location: storage room off northeast quadrant of Crypt.

MISCELLANEOUS SCULPTURE

CAPITALS: *Cornstalk or Corncob Columns and Capitals*, (six), designed by Benjamin Henry Latrobe, 1809; modeled by Giuseppe Franzoni; located in the first floor vestibule of the Old Supreme Court Chamber later the Law Library, opposite Room S–141.

Tobacco Capitals, designed by Benjamin Henry Latrobe; modeled and carved by Francisco Iardella in 1816; crown the 16 columns of the lobby of the small rotunda on the second floor, north of the main Rotunda. Tobacco is also used in the capitals of the 28 columns in the Hall of Columns, first floor, House wing; erected 1855–1856.

CLOCKS: *Car of History*, marble clock located upon the Gallery front, above the north entrance in Statuary Hall, by Carlo Franzoni, 1819. Clio, the Muse, representing History, stands in the winged car of Time, recording events as they occur. The car is placed upon a marble globe on which is carved in relief the Signs of the Zodiac. The face of the clock forms the chariot wheel.

Indian and the Pioneer, bronze clock by William H. Rinehart, 1857; removed and stored after the period of the remodeling of the House Chamber, 1940–1951.

EAGLES: *Eagle on the Frieze*, Statuary Hall. On the frieze of the entablature directly under the Statue of Liberty, is sculptured in stone, in relief, an eagle with outspread wings. This work of Giuseppe Valaperta, circa 1816, replaced an earlier eagle executed by Giuseppe Franzoni, destroyed in the fire of 1814.

Eagle, Old Supreme Court Chamber. This golden eagle has been located in the room known as the Old Supreme Court Chamber for a great many years. The first reference to such an eagle, found to date in the records of the National Archives was for the year 1834. In 1838 while the Chamber was occupied by the Senate, Daniel Webster refers to "the flag, the Eagle and the Stars and Stripes waving over the chamber in which we sit." In 1846 bills for repairs to the eagle and the shield are found, and in 1898 after the gas explosion, the eagle and the shield were again regilded and repaired. The actual date of its placing, the manufacturer, cost and other information has not yet been established.

FOUNTAIN, INDIAN—bronze, by William H. Rinehart, 1857; commissioned for the Old Post Office Building. It was brought to the Capitol in 1876 when the steps of the Post Office were changed in the grading of F Street. The fountain is located in the Office of the Architect of the Capitol, Room SB–14.

MASK, bronze, from the Chamber of the House of Representatives; located in the Architect's Office. Executed in 1857 and attributed to Joseph Wilson. This mask was to be one of fifteen (which were never executed) for the keystones over the doors of the House of Representatives. The mask was removed from the north doorway when the House Chamber was remodeled 1940–1951.

STATUETTES: *Pericles*, bronze statuette, by unlisted artist; located in the House Appropriations Committee Room, H–216; ownership uncertain.

Phideas, bronze statuette, by unlisted artist; located in the House Appropriations Committee Room, H–216; ownership uncertain.

STAIRWAYS, four bronze, two located in the House wing, two in the Senate wing; modeled by Edmond Baudin, cast by Archer, Warner, Miskey and Company, 1857–1859.

SEVRES VASES, four, gifts from the Republic of France in 1918; two are located in the Senators' private lobby adjacent to the Senate Chamber, and two relocated from the House Reading Room (Members' Retiring Room) to the House Reception Room, Capitol Extension, Room H–207, in May 1962. The dimensions of the vases are approximately 68¾″ high and 28″ in diameter.

MARY WASHINGTON MONUMENT: Miniature Model of the monument in Fredericksburg, Virginia. Miniature Model is stored in the Architect's Storeroom.

TOBACCO CAPITAL
Designed by Benjamin Henry Latrobe; modeled and carved by Francisco Iardella.
Location: Lobby of the small rotunda on the second floor, north of the main rotunda; also in the Hall of Columns, first floor, House wing.

CORNSTALK or CORNCOB CAPITAL (sandstone)
Designed by Benjamin Henry Latrobe; modeled by Giuseppe Franzoni.
Location: First floor vestibule of the Old Supreme Court Chamber.

354

CAR OF HISTORY
Marble clock by Carlo Franzoni.
Location: Statuary Hall.

355

EAGLE ON THE FRIEZE—Statuary Hall
Sculptured in stone by Giuseppe Valaperta.
Location: Frieze of the entablature below the Statue of Liberty.

EAGLE
Execution: Unknown.
Location: Old Supreme Court Chamber

INDIAN FOUNTAIN
Executed by William H. Rinehart.
Location: Office of the Architect of the Capitol.

357

BRONZE STAIRWAY, showing the newel post and lower section of railing.
Modeled by Edmond Baudin; cast by Archer, Warner, Miskey and Company.
Location: House wing, first floor level.

BRONZE STAIRWAY, showing section of railing.
Modeled by Edmond Baudin; cast by Archer, Warner, Miskey and Company.
Location: House wing, second floor level.

SEVRES VASES (4)
Gifts from the Republic of France.
Location: Two are located in the Senators' private lobby adjacent to the Senate Chamber and two are located in the House Reception Room, Capitol Extension (vases shown are located in the House Reception Room).

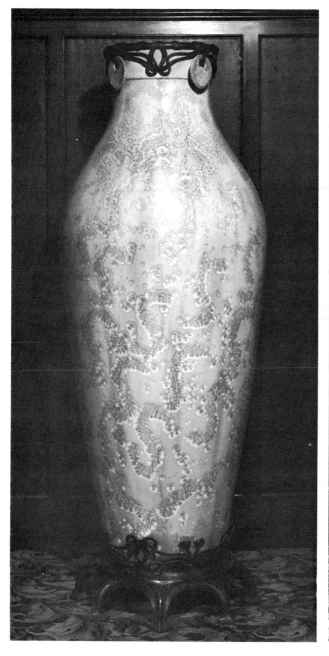

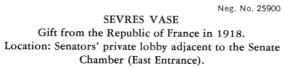

Neg. No. 25900

SEVRES VASE
Gift from the Republic of France in 1918.
Location: Senators' private lobby adjacent to the Senate
Chamber (East Entrance).

Neg. No. 25899

SEVRES VASE
Gift from the Republic of France in 1918.
Location: Senators' private lobby adjacent to the Senate
Chamber (West Entrance).

ART AND STAINED GLASS WINDOWS AND SKYLIGHTS

STAINED GLASS CIRCULAR WINDOWS (four) are above the first floor on each Grand Stairway. Executed 1859–1860 by the J. and G. H. Gibson Company of Philadelphia, Pennsylvania. Three windows are emblazoned with the shield, eagle and flags of the United States, and the motto, "E Pluribus Unum." The center portion of the fourth window on the East Senate Stairway was accidentally destroyed and was replaced with embossed glass. (No illustration.)

STAINED GLASS CIRCULAR SKYLIGHT, Vestibule of the Senate Chamber, Senate wing, East, third floor, was executed by Maria Herndl, in 1909–1910. The decorations are of conventional designs. (No illustration.)

STAINED GLASS RECTANGULAR SKYLIGHTS (three), Senate wing, East, second floor. Executed in 1859 by the J. and G. H. Gibson Company of Philadelphia, Pennsylvania. The decorations are of conventional designs.

STAINED GLASS CIRCULAR SKYLIGHT, Vestibule of the House Chamber, House wing, East, third floor. Records incomplete. The decorations are of conventional designs. (No illustration.)

STAINED GLASS CIRCULAR SKYLIGHT, located in the Senate Press Gallery, Senate wing, third floor. Executed by Maria Herndl in 1907. This skylight is decorated with six cherubs on a blue background. (No illustration.)

PRAYER ROOM WINDOW, H–234, was donated anonymously in 1955; located in the Prayer Room, adjacent to the Rotunda. The window speaks of that religious faith which has always been a part of the greatness of our Nation. The central figure is of the kneeling Washington. Other decorations include the Great Seal of the United States, the Bible, a biblical quotation, mottoes and names of the States.

GEORGE WASHINGTON MEMORIAL WINDOW, by Maria Herndl, executed in 1909–1910. The window represents a vivid patriotic scene of the Revolutionary War in 1780, depicting General Washington in conference with General Lafayette and Baron Von Steuben. Loaned to the Smithsonian Institution in 1932, it remained there until 1962, when it was returned and

installed in the Senators' Private Dining Room in the Senate wing, first floor, Capitol Extension.

STAINED GLASS SKYLIGHTS over four Grand Stairways, East and West, executed 1859–1860 by J. and G. H. Gibson Company of Philadelphia, Pennsylvania. These skylights are ornately decorated with medallions and panels of floral and fruit designs.

Neg. No. 11729

PRAYER ROOM WINDOW
Stained Glass Window donated anonymously.
Location: Prayer Room, adjacent to the Rotunda.

GEORGE WASHINGTON MEMORIAL WINDOW
Art Glass Window by Maria Herndl.
Location: Senators' Private Dining Room, Senate wing, first floor.

STAINED GLASS SKYLIGHT
Executed 1859–1860 by J. and G. H. Gibson Company of Philadelphia, Pennsylvania.
Location: Over the 4 Grand Stairways, East and West.

Exterior Works of Art in the United States Capitol

STATUE OF FREEDOM

The bronze statue surmounting the Dome of the United States Capitol, and facing to the East, is officially known as the Statue of Freedom. It was designed by Thomas Crawford in Rome, Italy in 1856 and the plaster model shipped to this country from Leghorn, Italy, April 19, 1858. It is 19 feet 6 inches high, weighs 14,985 pounds and cost exclusive of erecting in place, $23,796.82. On December 2, 1863 the last section of the Statue of Freedom was erected in place on the Dome of the Capitol. The motto, "E Pluribus Unum" is incised on the base. The statue was cast in the shops of Clark Mills, in Northeast Washington.

The figure is that of a woman clad in flowing draperies with her right hand resting upon the hilt of a sheathed sword and her left holding a wreath and grasping a shield. At the waist, a brooch bearing the letters "U.S." holds the drapery in place. The head is covered by a helmet encircled with stars and surmounted by a crest composed of an eagle's head and bold arrangement of feathers, suggested by the costume of our Indian tribes.

The original plaster model from which the bronze statue was cast is on exhibition in the old building of the National Museum in Washington, D.C.

Neg. No. 27751
STATUE OF FREEDOM
Bronze statue by Thomas Crawford.
Location: Surmounting the Dome of the United States Capitol.

DISCOVERY AND RESCUE GROUPS

THE DISCOVERY GROUP, statuary group by Luigi Persico; purchased in 1837–1844; erected in 1844; originally located on East Front steps, Central portico, south cheek block; stored at the Capitol Power Plant since 1958. Columbus holds aloft the globe, while an Indian maiden cowers at his side with surprise and awe.

THE RESCUE GROUP, statuary group by Horatio Greenough; purchased in 1837–1851; erected in 1853; originally located on East Front steps, Central portico, north cheek block; stored at the Capitol Power Plant since 1958. A frontiersman protects his wife and child from massacre by an Indian brave.

Neg. No. 100

THE DISCOVERY GROUP
Statuary group by Luigi Persico.
Location: In storage.

Neg. No. 102

THE RESCUE GROUP
Statuary group by Horatio Greenough.
Location: In storage.

STATUES OF JUSTICE AND HISTORY

Two statues by Thomas Crawford rest on a cap supported by massive brackets above the bronze door of the Senate wing, East Portico. Two female figures reclining against a globe represent Justice and History. Justice is supporting a volume bearing the inscription "Justice, Law, Order," a pair of scales lies by her right hand. History holds a scroll incised "History, July 1776." This work was installed in 1863.

Neg. No. 11745

JUSTICE AND HISTORY
Statues by Thomas Crawford.
(*Note:* Deterioration of figures due to elements.)
Location: Above the bronze door of the Senate wing, East Portico.

STATUES OF WAR AND PEACE

WAR: War is depicted as a male figure in the costume of the ancient Roman warrior. His countenance is firm and sedate, without any indication of rage or fury. He assumes the attitude of listening to Peace, who stands on his left. War is located in a niche north of the main entrance, East Central Portico.

PEACE: A female figure, draped in simple, flowing robes, holds in her left hand a fruit-bearing olive branch which she extends towards War. She gracefully points her hand to her bosom, indicating her sympathy for the condition of mankind. Peace is located in a niche south of the main entrance, East Central Portico.

The original statues were executed by Luigi Persico, 1833. The statues were reproduced in Vermont White Marble in 1959–1960. From the plaster models, executed by G. Giannetti, made from the originals as restored by Carl Schmitz, the reproductions were carved by carvers of the Vermont Marble Company, under the supervision of Paul Manship, for the extended East Central Front of the Capitol.

The plaster models of the statues of War and Peace are located in the Rotunda of the Cannon House Office Building, subway level. The original marble models are in storage.

Neg. No. 20505

WAR

Marble statue reproduced from the original by Luigi Persico. Restored by Carl Schmitz; plaster model by G. Giannetti; carved by carvers of Vermont Marble Company under the supervision of Paul Manship.

Location: In a niche north of the main entrance, East Central Portico.

Neg. No. 20504

PEACE

Marble statue reproduced from the original by Luigi Persico. Restored by Carl Schmitz; plaster model by G. Giannetti; carved by carvers of Vermont Marble Company under the supervision of Paul Manship.

Location: in a niche south of the main entrance, East Central Portico.

BRONZE DOORS

The bronze door at the eastern entrance to the Rotunda was designed and modeled by Randolph Rogers in Rome, Italy, in 1858 and cast in Munich, Germany, by Ferdinand von Miller at the Royal Bavarian Foundary in 1861.

In November 1863, the door was originally installed between Statuary Hall and the south extension, and in 1871, it was removed to the East Portico entrance. As part of the Extension of the Capitol Project, the door was moved to its present location in 1961 on the extended East Portico entrance. The overall dimensions, including the frame, are 16 feet 8 inches by 9 feet 9 inches.

The door is sometimes called the Rogers Door or Columbus Door. It has two valves, with four panels in each valve, and one semicircular transom over the entire door. The scenes depict events in the life of Christopher Columbus.

Columbus Before the Council of Salamanca, 1486–1487

Beginning at the bottom of the door on the left (south), the panel depicts Columbus undergoing an examination before the Council of Salamanca. He is seen here zealously unfolding his grand theory—a new route to the East—to a bigoted audience. At last, after long delays, the Council declared the project vain and impossible.

Columbus' Departure From the Convent of La Rabida, 1492

Columbus' departure from the Convent of La Rabida, near Palos, depicts him just setting out to visit the Spanish Court. It was to this Convent he had come with his small son Diego, weary, penniless and discouraged. He was befriended by Juan Perez, prior of the Convent and Confessor to Queen Isabella, and by Lady Bobadilla, an attendant of Isabella. The Queen had been induced to assist Columbus in his expedition.

Audience At the Court of Ferdinand and Isabella, 1492

This panel pictures Queen Isabella, seated in state, leaning forward and seemingly deeply interested in what Columbus is saying. King Ferdinand, by her side, with chilling apathy, evidently regards him as a visionary. On April 17, 1492 the agreement between Columbus and their Majesties was signed.

Departure of Columbus From Palos, August 3, 1492

The town of Palos had been ordered to find two ships. Three were given Columbus—the "Niña," the "Pinta" and the "Santa Maria." The panel depicts Columbus confiding his son to the monks before he embarks upon his first voyage. His ships lie waiting in the harbor. Columbus made four voyages in all to the New World—1492, 1493, 1498 and 1502.

The Landing of Columbus in the New World, October 12, 1492

The transom panel occupies the semicircular sweep over the whole door. It depicts the first landing of Columbus and the Spaniards in state at Guanahani, Watling Island, called San Salvador by Columbus, October 12, 1492.

Columbus' First Encounter With the Indians

Beginning at the top of the door on the right (north), this panel contains the first of the sad scenes of the door, and represents the earliest encounter of the discoverers with the natives. In it one of the sailors is seen bringing an Indian girl on his shoulders a prisoner. This action aroused the stern indignation of Columbus.

Entry of Columbus Into Barcelona, 1493

The triumphal entry of Columbus into Barcelona, where the Court was sitting, is full of the glory of success and waving banners. All the halo of rose-color seems now to light up the future of the great Discoverer.

Columbus in Chains, 1500

Don Francisco de Bobadilla, sent out by the Court to investigate charges preferred against Columbus, had him placed in chains and returned to Spain, November 1500. On board the vessel, the officers wished to relieve him of his chains, but Columbus replied with deep feeling, "I will wear them as a memento of the gratitude of princes."

Columbus was cleared of the charges, and in 1502 set sail once more, determined to find a strait to Portuguese Asia. He remained in the New World until 1504, when plagued by his own illness and the lawlessness of his followers, he again set sail from Jamaica to return to Spain, September 12, 1504.

Death of Columbus, 1506

Columbus had returned from his last voyage poor, sick and disconsolate. He sought redress at the Spanish Court, and although he had been cleared of all the charges against him, he failed in his attempt. With the death of Queen Isabella in 1504, Columbus had lost his influence at the Court.

The last panel is the death scene. The last rites of the Catholic Church have been administered—friends and attendants are around him—and a priest holds up a crucifix for him to kiss, and upon it bids him fix his dying eyes.

"Columbus died at Valladolid, the 20th of May, 1506. His last words were, 'Into thy hands, O Lord, I commend my spirit.' Those closing eyes doubtless opened upon a new discovery—that far brighter land than the Western Antilles * * *" (Wyeth, "The Federal City, 1865").

The Statuettes

On the door, on the sides and between these panels, are sixteen small statues, set in niches, of eminent contemporaries of Columbus. Their names are marked on the door, as well as on the diagram, where they are printed in the positions they occupy on the door.

Beginning at the bottom, on the side from which we started in numbering the panels, we find the figure occupying the lowest niche on the chart is

Perez. Juan Perez de Marchena was prior of the Convent of La Rabida, the early and ever firm friend of Columbus.

The niche above this is occupied by *Cortez*, the conqueror of Mexico.

Above him again stands *Ojeda*. Don Alonzo de Ojeda was an early Spanish adventurer to the New World, but lacked fealty to Columbus.

Vespucci occupies the next niche on the door. It is, perhaps, not generally known that among the friends of Columbus whom he trusted during his last dark days was numbered Amerigo Vespucci.

Then come, opposite in line across the door, standing in two niches, side by side, *Mendoza* and *Alexander VI*. Pedro Gonzales de Mendoza, Arch-

bishop of Toledo and Grand Cardinal of Spain, at an early period patronized the cause of Columbus. His influence at court was great. Alexander VI was a Roman Pontiff. He was a native of Valencia and born a subject to the crown of Aragon. He was an able and politic sovereign.

Then follow, below them, *Isabella* and *Ferdinand*, King and Queen of Spain.

Beneath them stands the *Lady Beatrix de Bobadilla*, marchioness of Moya, the early friend of Columbus, and favorite of Queen Isabella. Beside her is

Charles VIII, King of France, a prince of the house of Valois.

The first figure of the lowest pair on the door is *Henry VII*, of England. He was a patron of navigation, and seemed disposed to regard with favor the theory of Columbus, which was presented to his notice by Bartholomew, the brother of the Admiral. Beside him, stands

John II, King of Portugal. This monarch declined accepting the proposals from Columbus made him previous to his application to Ferdinand and Isabella. Then in the same line with them, across the panel, is

Pinzon. Martin Alonzo Pinzon commanded the "Pinta," one of Columbus' little fleet of three vessels. It was he who first saw "Land," September 25, 1492. Eventually his friendship died out, and he proved treacherous to Columbus. In the niche above Pinzon stands *B. Columbus*, the brother of the Admiral, and appointed by him lieutenant-governor of the Indies. Then comes

Vasco Nuñez de Balboa, a Spanish discoverer and adventurer. It was he who crossed the Isthmus of Darien and on September 29, 1510, first saw from a mountain the Pacific Ocean. In the niche above, again at the top of the door, stands the figure of *Francisco Pizarro*, the conqueror of Peru.

The Heads on the Door

Between the panels and at top and bottom of the valves of the door are ten small heads. They are indicated on the diagram by round outline dots. These heads represent historians who have written on Columbus' voyages from his own time down to the 1860's—ending with Irving and Prescott. Of the four female heads, two appear to be Indians. Above the transom arch are the bust of Columbus, the American Eagle and flags. The door is covered with heraldic emblems of that period.

BRONZE DOOR—Rotunda (Columbus Door)
Designed and modeled by Randolph Rogers.
Location: Eastern entrance to the Rotunda.

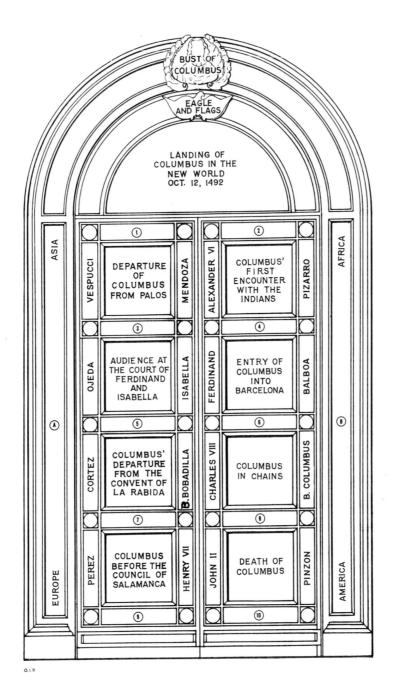

BUST OF
COLUMBUS

EAGLE
AND FLAGS

LANDING OF
COLUMBUS IN THE
NEW WORLD
OCT. 12, 1492

ASIA · AFRICA · EUROPE · AMERICA

VESPUCCI · MENDOZA · ALEXANDER VI · PIZARRO

OJEDA · ISABELLA · FERDINAND · BALBOA

CORTEZ · B. BOBADILLA · CHARLES VIII · B. COLUMBUS

PEREZ · HENRY VII · JOHN II · PINZON

① DEPARTURE OF COLUMBUS FROM PALOS

② COLUMBUS' FIRST ENCOUNTER WITH THE INDIANS

③ AUDIENCE AT THE COURT OF FERDINAND AND ISABELLA

④ ENTRY OF COLUMBUS INTO BARCELONA

⑤ COLUMBUS' DEPARTURE FROM THE CONVENT OF LA RABIDA

⑥ COLUMBUS IN CHAINS

⑦ COLUMBUS BEFORE THE COUNCIL OF SALAMANCA

⑧ DEATH OF COLUMBUS

Ⓐ Ⓑ

DIAGRAM OF BRONZE DOORS OF THE
MAIN ENTRANCE TO ROTUNDA - EAST FRONT
UNITED STATES CAPITOL

1 0 1 2 FT.

O.I.P.

Neg. No. 26503

371

The bronze door at the entrance of the East Portico, House wing, second floor, was designed by Thomas Crawford in Rome, Italy in 1855–1857. Upon the death of Crawford, William H. Rinehart executed the models from the Crawford sketches, 1863–1867.

The models were shipped from Leghorn, Italy in 1867. They were stored in the Crypt of the United States Capitol, and in 1903–1904 were cast by Melzar H. Mosman of Chicopee, Massachusetts. The door was installed in 1905.

The bronze door of the House wing resembles in general outline the arrangement of the Senate door. Each valve, or door, consists of three panels and a medallion depicting great events in American history:

Medallion—Death of General Montgomery, December 31, 1775

Beginning at the bottom of the door on the left (south), the medallion depicts the death of General Montgomery. Late in 1775, Congress sent a two column military expedition to Canada—one under Richard Montgomery via New York, and the other under Benedict Arnold via Maine—hoping to arouse the French Canadians to revolt against the British. The expedition failed. In the attack on Quebec, December 31, 1775, General Montgomery was killed.

Presentation of Flag and Medal to General Nathanael Greene, 1781

In 1778 Great Britain shifted the attack upon the colonies to the South. Nathanael Greene replaced General Gates as Commander in the South and with the help of bands of loyal American frontiersmen, the British camps were raided. By 1781 the British had been pushed back to where they were in 1778. This panel depicts General Greene receiving a medal and flag after the Battle of Eutaw Springs on September 8, 1781 for expelling the British from South Carolina.

Battle of Lexington, April 19, 1775

General Gage, the British Commander in Boston, had heard that the Colonists were collecting arms and ammunition. He determined to prevent rebellion by seizing these supplies. The colonists were warned and during the night of April 18, 1775, Paul Revere and William Dawes rode to warn the Minutemen. The British troops were marching toward Concord and met the small Militia. Here on April 19, 1775 occurred the famous "shot heard 'round the World"—the beginning of the Revolutionary War.

Massacre of Wyoming, Pennsylvania, July 3, 1778

During the Revolution a large proportion of the men of Wyoming Valley, Pennsylvania joined the Continental Army. A number of Loyalists remained there, however, and in 1778, they were joined by British troops and their Indian allies. The settlers who had taken refuge in Forty Fort, near Wilkes-Barre, outnumbered 1100 to 400, were attacked. After a desperate battle, the settlers were forced to capitulate. The massacre followed.

Medallion—Benjamin Franklin in His Studio

This medallion is the first panel beginning at the bottom of the door on the right (north). It depicts Benjamin Franklin, who was an inventor, a Signer of the Declaration of Independence and the Constitution; a Member of the Continental Congress and Minister to France, 1776–1785. He gained liberal concessions for the United States of America at the Signing of the Treaty of Paris in 1783.

Washington's Farewell to His Officers in New York, December 4, 1783

After the Revolution, Washington was about to leave New York to go to Philadelphia. His officers who had stood by him during the long dreary war years gathered at Fraunces Tavern to say good-bye. When he entered the room he could scarcely command his voice. He spoke briefly, and they drank a toast. Washington requested each man to come forward and take his hand. General Knox, who stood nearest, was first to clasp his hand. The panel depicts this touching farewell.

The Signing of the Treaty at Paris Between the United States and Great Britain, September 3, 1783

The Revolution ended in October 1781, but it was not until 1783 that the final treaty, called the

Treaty of Paris, was signed. The panel depicts the negotiations between the United States commissioners and the British representatives. The liberal concessions to the United States were largely due to the efforts of Benjamin Franklin.

Public Reading of the Declaration of Independence at Philadelphia, July 8, 1776

On June 7, 1776, Richard Henry Lee of Virginia introduced a resolution in the Second Continental Congress declaring "these United Colonies are, and of right ought to be free and independent states." A committee was appointed and a declaration drafted and discussed. On July 4, 1776, after making several alterations, Congress adopted the Declaration of Independence. It was signed by John Hancock and other delegates, and copies were prepared and rushed to the legislatures of the newly created states. Finally, on July 8, 1776, the Declaration of Independence was officially proclaimed in Philadelphia. This panel depicts this first public reading.

The overall dimensions of the door, including the frame, are 14 feet 7 inches by 7 feet 4 inches.

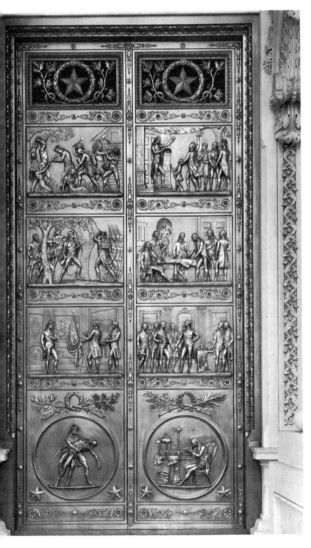

Neg. No. 22711

BRONZE DOOR—House wing
Designed by Thomas Crawford; executed by William H. Rinehart.
Location: East House Portico, second floor entrance.

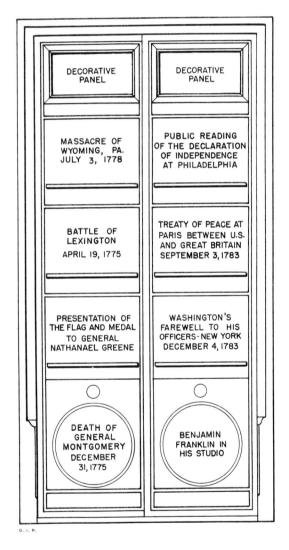

DIAGRAM OF BRONZE DOORS OF THE HOUSE WING - UNITED STATES CAPITOL

Neg. No. 26505

373

The bronze door at the entrance of the East Portico, Senate wing, second floor, was designed and modeled by Thomas Crawford in 1855–1857 in Rome, Italy. The plaster models were completed after Mr. Crawford's death by William H. Rinehart and shipped to America in 1864.

The door was cast by James T. Ames at the foundry in Chicopee, Massachusetts in 1864–1868 and placed late in 1868.

The scenes depict events in the life of George Washington and the early history of our country. One valve illustrates important events during the Revolutionary War; the other valve depicts events after the War. Each valve, or door, consists of three panels and a medallion:

Allegorical Medallion of War

Beginning at the bottom of the door on the right (north), depicting war scenes, the first panel is an allegorical representation of War. In the medallion of this panel, a Hessian soldier is in a death struggle with the farmer, as he protects his wife and child from the soldier's assault.

Battle of Yorktown and the Gallantry of Alexander Hamilton, 1781

The scene is at the close of the war when Cornwallis was entrenched at Yorktown, Virginia. At Hamilton's earnest personal request to General Washington, he was allowed to lead the attack on one of the two redoubts that had to be taken. The center figure of this panel is Alexander Hamilton, gallantly leading the attack.

Battle of Monmouth and the Rebuke of General Lee, 1778

On June 18, 1778, the British Army evacuated Philadelphia and proceeded through New Jersey toward New York. General Charles Lee and General Lafayette were in command of the Militia that was to harass the rear of the British Army in order to bring on a general engagement. A successful attack was made, but Lee failed to hold the ground. General Washington met the retreating troops, and rallied them. The panel depicts General Washington rebuking General Lee with great severity for his failure to obey his orders.

Battle of Bunker Hill and the Death of General Warren, 1775

On June 16, 1775, the British Army, under General Gage, intended to seize and fortify Bunker Hill, opposite the City of Boston. Under cover of darkness that night, Colonel Prescott, with a thousand American patriots, entrenched themselves on Breed's Hill, lower, but nearer Boston. The British determined to dislodge the Americans at any cost. At 3 P.M. the following day, the ships in the harbor opened fire upon the redoubt, and the British then moved in perfect order up Breed's Hill. Generals Putnam and Warren had joined Prescott, and it was Putnam who uttered those well-remembered words, "reserve your fire until you see the whites of the enemies' eyes." The Americans ran out of ammunition and were forced to retreat, and General Warren, last to leave, was shot by a musket ball. In the panel, Colonel Prescott is shown supporting the form of the dying General Warren.

Allegorical Medallion of Peace

Beginning at the bottom of the door on the left (south), depicting events in the early history of our country, is an allegorical representation of Peace and Agriculture. The scene is quietly beautiful, and in it are included figures in Infancy, Maternity, Childhood, Youth, and Manhood, grouped about a plow, upon which is a sheaf of wheat. The Youth holds a book in his hand.

Ovation For George Washington At Trenton, New Jersey, 1789

On April 16, 1789, George Washington formally accepted his election to the office of President of the United States at a dinner in Alexandria, Virginia, on his way to New York to enter upon his office. Every city and hamlet along his route gave him an ovation. The panel depicts George Washington receiving the ovation at Trenton, New Jersey. Over the bridge of Assumpink Creek, on the banks of which Washington had defeated the British, a triumphal arch of flowers was built. Small girls strewed flowers before him as he slowly rode across the bridge, accompanied by the singing of the multitudes gathered to honor him.

BRONZE DOOR—Senate wing
Designed and modeled by Thomas Crawford; completed
by William H. Rinehart.
Location: East Senate Portico, second floor entrance.

*Inauguration of George Washington As First President,
1789*

The inauguration took place April 30, 1789 on the balcony in front of Federal Hall in New York City. A table was covered with crimson velvet, and on it the open Bible rested upon a velvet cushion. Chancellor Livingston is depicted administering the oath of office, and George Washington's right hand is resting upon the open Bible. John Adams, Vice President, is shown on the right, with other noted guests at the left of the panel. The Bible used on this occasion is now the property of St. John's Lodge, No. 1, A.Y.M. and F. and A.M. of New York City.

*Laying of the Cornerstone of the United States Capitol,
1793*

On September 18, 1793, the Cornerstone of the United States Capitol was laid in the southeast corner of the north wing, with Masonic rites, by President George Washington. This panel shows George Washington with the trowel in his right hand, laying the suitably inscribed silver plate upon the Cornerstone. It is interesting to note that the silver trowel and masonic apron used on this occasion are in the possession of the Alexandria-Washington Lodge, No. 22, A.F. and A.M. of Alexandria; the marble-headed gavel is owned by Potomac Lodge, No. 5, F.A.A.M. of Washington, D.C. These, and the Bible, have been used at other cornerstone layings.

The overall dimensions of the door, including the frame, are 14 feet 5½ inches by 7 feet 4 inches.

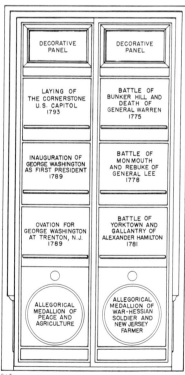

DIAGRAM OF BRONZE DOORS OF THE
SENATE WING - UNITED STATES CAPITOL

Louis Amateis of Washington, D.C. designed and modeled in 1904 a bronze door intended for the western entrance of the Capitol. It was cast in 1909 by Jno. Williams, Incorporated, in New York City, New York and was received in Washington, D.C. July 1910. As enabling legislation for the improvement of the West Front had not been enacted, the door could not be placed. It was temporarily exhibited at the Corcoran Gallery of Art, 1910–1914. Since February 1914, it has been on loan to the Smithsonian Institution until such a time as the West Front improvements are accomplished. This door is currently exhibited in the foyer of the Natural History Building, Smithsonian Institution, 10th Street and Constitution Avenue, N.W., Washington, D.C.

The door is sometimes called the Amateis Door. It has two valves, with four panels in each valve, and a rectangular transom over the entire door. The transom portrays the Apotheosis of America. The panels represent: Jurisprudence, Science, Fine Arts, Mining, Agriculture, Iron and Electricity, Engineering and Naval Architecture, and Commerce. Famous men are depicted in statuettes and medallions, and allegorical representations are used in the transom.

Transom

Subject: Apotheosis of America

America, in a chariot drawn by Lions, is symbolic of Strength. The Lion is led by a Child, signifying the superiority of the intellect over brute force. At the sides of the chariot are allegorical figures of Education, Architecture, Painting, Literature, Music, Sculpture, Commerce, Mining and Industry.

Medallions in the four corners:
1. George Peabody—Educational Institutions.
2. Ralph Waldo Emerson—Philosophy.
3. Horace Mann—Education.
4. John Hopkins—Philanthropist.

On the right side of the transom is the figure of Thomas Jefferson and on the left side of the transom is the figure of Benjamin Franklin. The panels contain scenes depicting the following:

Left Valve

I. Jurisprudence (upper left) represented by the Supreme Court presided over by Justice John Marshall. The bust of George Washington is shown over the chair of the Chief Justice. Statuettes at the right and left represent James Madison and Daniel Webster.

Above are medallions of Patrick Henry, Chief Justice Roger B. Taney, and Rufus Choate.

II. Science Panel: Scientific workers from Hipparchus of Egypt, inventor of the planiscope, down to Charles R. Darwin. At the sides are statuettes of Oliver W. Gibbs, chemist, and Joseph Henry, physicist. The medallions portray Simon Newcomb, astronomer; Alexander Graham Bell, inventor of the telephone; Samuel F. B. Morse, inventor of the telegraph, and James D. Dana, geologist.

III. Fine Arts Panel: Figures of Virgil, Dante, Shakespeare, Goethe, Hugo, Palestrina, Beethoven, Rossini, and Homer. Above them is a flying figure of Genius. The statuettes at the sides are of Edgar Allen Poe, writer, and William Thornton, first Architect of the U.S. Capitol. The medallions portray Gilbert Stuart, painter, and Henry Kirke Brown, sculptor.

IV. Mining Panel: Scene at a mine. On one side of this panel are statuettes of James W. Marshall, discoverer of gold in California, and on the other side is Alexander Holley, mining engineer. The medallions portray E. C. Case, Abram Hewett, and Clarence King.

Right Valve

I. Agriculture. The top panel on the right side of the door shows a harvest scene, typical of Agriculture. The statuettes are of Samuel G. Morton, a naturalist, at one side and, James Wilson, agriculturist, at the other. The medallions portray Senator Justin S. Morrill, John Pitkin Norton, agricultural chemist, and Benjamin Bussey, agricultural chemist.

II. Iron and Electricity Panel depicts a scene in which iron and electric workers are shown. The statuettes are of Peter Cooper, philanthropist, and Henry A. Rowland, physicist. Medallions show Matthias W. Baldwin, founder of the locomotive works, and Thomas Alva Edison, inventor.

III. Engineering Panel, scene of workers laying a railroad track. A bridge is in the background. Statuettes show James B. Eads, builder of the St. Louis bridge, and Thomas L. Casey,

Army Engineer. Medallions portray Washington A. Roebling, builder of the Brooklyn bridge and Edwin A. Stevens builder of the transcontinental railroads.

IV. NAVAL ARCHITECTURE, AND COMMERCE: Panel represented by the figure of Youth, symbolic of Naval Architecture, showing Commerce, Industry, and Agriculture on a Globe where they dispose of their wares. The sailor is represented holding a flag surmounted by a liberty cap, signifying the open door policy. Statuettes portray Robert Fulton, inventor of the steamboat, and John Ericsson, inventor of the Monitor.

Medallions:

Cyrus W. Field—Atlantic Cable.

Eli Whitney—Cotton Gin.

Elias Howe—Sewing Machine.

John C. Fremont—The Pathfinder.

John Lenthall—Naval Constructor.

The overall dimensions, including the ornamental frame, are 13 feet 10 inches by 7 feet 3½ inches.

Neg. No. 24609

BRONZE DOOR—Executed for the West Front
Designed and modeled by Louis Amateis.
Location: Stored—Smithsonian Institution.

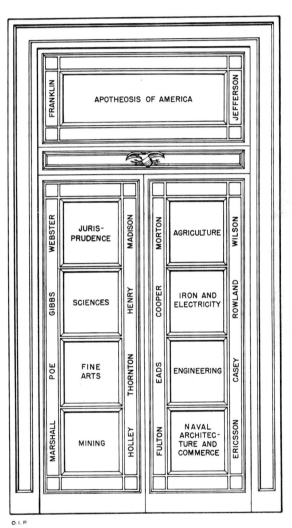

DIAGRAM OF BRONZE DOORS
DESIGNED AND CAST FOR THE WEST
FRONT - MAIN CENTRAL ENTRANCE
UNITED STATES CAPITOL

Neg. No. 26506

377

PEDIMENTS

PEDIMENT OVER CENTRAL PORTICO, EAST FRONT: "Genius of America."

America, the central figure, rests her right arm on a shield, inscribed "U.S.A." and supported by an altar or pedestal bearing the inscription "July 4, 1776." To the right, she points to Justice holding the scales and in her right hand a scroll is inscribed "Constitution, 17 September 1787." To the left of America is an Eagle and the figure of Hope, who rests an arm on an anchor—the whole intended to convey that while we cultivate justice, we may strive for success.

The original sandstone figures were executed by Luigi Persico in 1825–1828 after a design suggested by President John Quincy Adams. In 1959–1960 during the Extension of the Capitol Project, the figures were restored by Carl Schmitz, plaster models were made by G. Giannetti and carved in Georgia White marble by Bruno Mankowski, all under the supervision of Paul Manship. Pediment: 81 feet 6 inches in length, with bold figures 9 feet in height.

The plaster model of the Central Pediment is located in the Rotunda of the Cannon House Office Building, subway level. The original sandstone model is in storage.

Neg. No. 20892

PEDIMENT—Central Section
Statuary: Original sandstone figures by Luigi Persico. Reproduced in marble from restored figures by Carl Schmitz, plaster model by G. Giannetti, carved by Bruno Mankowski—all under the supervision of Paul Manship. Location: Over Central Portico, East Front.

PEDIMENT OVER HOUSE PORTICO, EAST FRONT: "The Apotheosis of Democracy" by Paul Wayland Bartlett.

An allegorical group consisting of two figures, "Peace Protecting Genius," fills the center of the pediment. Peace, an armed Peace, stands erect, draped in a mantle which almost completely hides her breastplate and coat of mail; her left arm rests on her buckler, which is supported by the altar at her side; in the background the olive tree of peace. Her right arm is extended in a gesture of protection over the youthful and winged figure of Genius, who nestles confidingly at her feet and holds in his right hand the torch of Immortality. The composition is completed by two other groups, symbolizing and typifying the two great fundamental powers of labor, the two great sources of wealth—Agriculture and Industry. A wave terminates the sculpture at either end of the pediment and is meant to indicate that all this humanity, all its power and energy, are comprised between the shores of the two oceans—the Atlantic and Pacific.

The figures were modeled in Paris, France and Washington, D.C. in 1911–1914; carved in Georgia White marble by the Piccirilli Brothers of New York City, 1914–1916 and unveiled August 2, 1916. Extreme length of pediment 80 feet, height at center about 12 feet; length of sculpture about 60 feet.

The original model was made a gift to the United States Government in March 1963 by Mrs. Armistead Peter III, a stepdaughter of Paul Bartlett. It is being restored by G. Giannetti and will be placed in the new subway terminal at the west end of the House wing of the Capitol.

Neg. No. 11339

PEDIMENT—House wing
Statuary by Paul Wayland Bartlett.
Location: Over the East Front Portico of the House wing.

PEDIMENT OVER SENATE PORTICO, EAST FRONT:
"The Progress of Civilization" by Thomas Crawford.

The center figure is America with the Eagle at her side and the sun at her back. On her left the sculptured figures of the woodsman, the three Indian figures and the Indian grave, symbolic of death, portray the decline of the Indian race. On her right the progress of civilization is depicted in the figures of the soldier, merchant, two youths, the schoolmaster and child, and the mechanic. Completing this side of the pediment are sheaves of wheat, symbolic of fertility, and an anchor, symbolic of hope, in contradistinction to the grave at the opposite end of the sculpture of the Pediment.

The figures were modeled in Rome, Italy in 1854; carved of marble from the quarries at Lee, Massachusetts in the United States at the United States Capitol in 1855–1859 and erected in 1863. The carvers of the figures of the Senate Pediment were: T. Gagliardi, Vincenzo Casoni, G. Butti, Louis Galli, G. Caprero and Domenico Giampaoli.

The Extreme length of the Pediment is 80 feet, height at center about 12 feet and the length of the sculpture is about 60 feet.

PEDIMENT—Senate wing
Statuary by Thomas Crawford.
Location: Over the East Front Portico of the Senate wing.

Neg. No. 11338

STATUE OF CHIEF JUSTICE JOHN MARSHALL

(CAPITOL GROUNDS)

The bronze statue of John Marshall is a seated statue in judicial robes by William Wetmore Story, unveiled May 10, 1884. On the base is incised: "John Marshall, Chief Justice of the United States. Erected by the Bar and the Congress of the United States, A. D. MDCCCLXXXIV." On the north side of the base is a relief in white marble representing "Minerva Dictating the Constitution to Young America." On the south side, the relief represents "Victory Leading Young America to Swear Fidelity at the Altar of the Union." The sculptor has given us the posture of Marshall as the great jurist, sitting in the chair he used for so many years, rendering a judicial decision.

The statue is located at the foot of the terrace on the west plaza, West Front between the two stairways.

JOHN MARSHALL, Chief Justice of the United States
Statue by William Wetmore Story.
Location: Capitol Grounds, West Front.

ROBERT A. TAFT MEMORIAL

The Taft Memorial was designed by Douglas W. Orr, Architect, and is intended to interpret the man it honors by its simple strength and quiet dignity. The shaft of the tower of Tennessee marble is 100 feet high, 11 feet thick and 32 feet in width. It rests on a base 55 by 45 feet in area and 15 feet high. Jets of water play into a basin at the base. Twenty-seven bells cast in the Paccard Bell Foundry in Annecy, France, are hung in the upper part of the tower. At the base is a ten foot bronze statue of Robert A. Taft by Wheeler Williams, Sculptor.

Above it are incised these words:

> This Memorial to Robert A. Taft, presented by the people to the Congress of the United States, stands as tribute to the honesty, indomitable courage and high principles of free government symbolized by his life.

The memorial was dedicated April 14, 1959.

It is located in Square 633 in the United States Capitol Grounds, bounded by New Jersey Avenue on the East, Constitution Avenue on the south, C Street on the north, Louisiana Avenue diagonally on the northwest, and First Street on the west.

Neg. No. 20747

ROBERT A. TAFT MEMORIAL
Designed by Douglas W. Orr, Architect.
Bronze statue by Wheeler Williams.
Location: United States Capitol Grounds.

Portraits, Paintings, Photographs and Busts

(PROPERTY OF THE COMMITTEES)

PORTRAITS OF CHAIRMEN OF COMMITTEES

(NO ILLUSTRATIONS)

House Agriculture Committee

Five portraits; located in Committee Room 1310, Longworth House Office Building.

HAROLD D. COOLEY, by Mabel Pugh
JOHN W. FLANNAGAN, by Dalton Shourds
HAMPTON P. FULMER, by Dalton Shourds
CLIFFORD R. HOPE, by Mabel Pugh
MARVIN JONES, by Boris Gordon

House Armed Services Committee

One plaster bust and two portraits; located in Committee Room 313, Cannon House Office Building.

WALTER GRESHAM ANDREWS (plaster bust)
DEWEY SHORT, by P. A. Leason
CARL VINSON, by Lawrence Powers (gift to Naval Affairs Committee in 1944 by friends and colleagues; presented by House Naval Affairs Committee to House Armed Services Committee)

House Banking and Currency Committee

Two portraits; located in Committee Room 1301, Longworth House Office Building.

BRENT SPENCE, by Sam Gholson
HENRY B. STEAGALL, by Howard Chandler Christy

House Foreign Affairs Committee

Nine portraits; located in Committee Rooms H–320–321, Capitol.

SOL BLOOM, by Howard Chandler Christy
ROBERT B. CHIPERFIELD
CHARLES A. EATON, by A. Jonniaux
HENRY D. FLOOD, by M. Hartman
THOMAS S. GORDON
JOHN KEE, by A. Jonniaux
J. CHARLES LINTHICUM, by T. C. Corner
SAMUEL DAVIS MCREYNOLDS, by Henry Wolff
JAMES P. RICHARDS

House Interstate and Foreign Commerce Committee

Two portraits; located in Committee Room 1334, Longworth House Office Building.

OREN HARRIS, by Louis Freund
CHARLES A. WOLVERTON, by C. Ricciardi

House Judiciary Committee

Three portraits; located in Committee Room 346, Cannon House Office Building.

EMANUEL CELLER, by Joseph Margulies (gift from friends of the chairman—1963)
GEORGE S. GRAHAM, by unlisted artist (gift to the Committee)
HATTON SUMNERS, by Boris Gordon

House Merchant Marine and Fisheries Committee

Two portraits; located in Committee Room 219, Cannon House Office Building.

SCHUYLER OTIS BLAND, by unlisted Coast Guardsman
HERBERT BONNER, by Mabel Pugh

383

House Public Works Committee

Four portraits; located in Committee Room 1302; Longworth House Office Building.

   Charles A. Buckley, by Oscar Gruber
   George A. Dondero, by Dorothy Hart Drew
   Joseph J. Mansfield, by Boris Gordon
   William M. Whittington, by Karl Wolfe

House Veterans' Affairs Committee

Three portraits; located in Committee Room 356, Cannon House Office Building.

   Royal C. Johnson, by Margaret Brisbane (presented by American Legion)
   John E. Rankin, by Mrs. Brisbane Preble (presented by American Legion, Department of Mississippi)
   Edith Nourse Rogers, by Howard Chandler Christy (presented by the Committee on Veterans' Affairs, Department of Massachusetts)

House Ways and Means Committee

Fourteen portraits and one tinted photograph; located in Committee Room 1102, Longworth House Office Building.

   James William Collier, by Boris Gordon
   Jere Cooper, by Boris Gordon
   Nelson Dingley, Jr., by unknown artist
   Robert Lee Doughton, by Boris Gordon
   Joseph Warren Fordney (photograph tinted in oil)
   William Raymond Green, by unknown artist
   Willis Chatman Hawley, by Boris Gordon
   Claude Kitchin, by Freeman Thorp
   Harold Knutson, by Thomas E. Stephens
   William McKinley, Jr., by Freeman Thorp
   Roger Quarles Mills, by unknown artist
   Wilbur D. Mills, by Boris Gordon
   Sereno Elisha Payne, by Cecilia Beaux
   Daniel Alden Reed, by Jean Spencer
   Oscar W. Underwood, by Michel Jacobs
   Robert L. Doughton (enlarged photograph tinted in oil); located in Room H–208, Capitol. This tinted photograph was formerly carried on the records as the property of Mr. Doughton.

PAINTINGS

Iwo Jima, two paintings by Joseph Capolino. Presented to the House and Senate Armed Services Committees from the United States Marine Corps. Located in the respective Committee Rooms, Room 313, Cannon House Office Building and Room 212, Senate Office Building.

Works of Art Transferred to the New Building for the Supreme Court of the United States

(NO ILLUSTRATIONS)

There were in the Capitol for many years, a large number of works of art belonging to the United States Supreme Court. There still remain in the old courtroom of the United States Supreme Court in the Capitol Building, the busts of John Jay, John Rutledge, Oliver Ellsworth, John Marshall, Roger B. Taney, Salmon P. Chase, Morrison R. Waite, Melville W. Fuller, Edward D. White and William Howard Taft; all the foregoing being Chief Justices of the United States.

In addition to the sculptural work heretofore listed, there were located in the robing room the following oil portraits which have been removed to the new Supreme Court Building: John Jay, Roger B. Taney, Oliver Ellsworth, John Marshall, Salmon P. Chase, Morrison R. Waite, and John Rutledge, and a second protrait of John Marshall. The portrait of Chief Justice Marshall by St. Memin had also been given a place in the robing room.

The portrait of Chief Justice Edward D. White by Albert Rosenthal, a portrait of Chief Justice Taft by Ernest L. Ipsen, as well as a portrait of Associate Justice Story by G. P. A. Healy were removed to the new building.

There were also removed a marble bust of Associate Justice McLean by Benjamin Paul Akers, a marble bust of Chief Justice Roger B. Taney by Horatio Stone, and a marble bust of Justice Story by his son, W. W. Story, formerly occupying a place in the law library.

The following portraits of Clerks of the Supreme Court were removed to the new building of the United States Supreme Court: John Tucker, Samuel Bayard, E. B. Caldwell, William Griffith, William T. Carroll, Daniel Wesley Middleton, James H. McKenney, James D. Maher, and William R. Stansbury.

From the reporters' room of the Supreme Court there were removed portraits of Alexander James Dallas, William Cranch, Henry Wheaton, Richard Peters, Benjamin Chew Howard, Jeremiah S. Black, John William Wallace, William Todd Otto, and John C. Bancroft Davis, former reporters of the Supreme Court.

Works of Art Transferred From the Capitol

Chandelier

CRYSTAL CHANDELIER—Large chandelier used in the White House and removed during the remodeling in 1902–03 and sent to auction. Before the sale it was transferred to the Capitol for use there. In June 1962 this chandelier was removed from the Capitol to the White House on loan.

CRYSTAL CHANDELIER
Removed from the Senate Connecting Corridor, second floor, in June 1962.
On loan to the White House.

Neg. No. 22469

CHASM OF THE COLORADO, by Thomas Moran; acquired by purchase in 1874; transferred to the Department of the Interior in 1950, by provisions of Public Law 603, 81st Congress, 2nd Session, approved July 10, 1950. Painting located in Interior Department Museum.

FARMING IN THE DAKOTAS, by Carl Gutherz; transferred to the Department of Agriculture in 1888, by direction of the Joint Committee on the Library. (No illustration.)

FIRST FIGHT OF IRONCLADS, THE MONITOR AND MERRIMAC, by William Halsall; acquired by purchase in 1887; transferred to the United States Naval Academy at Annapolis in 1946 by provisions of Public Law 700, 79th Congress, 2nd Session, approved August 8, 1946. (No illustration.)

GRAND CANYON OF THE YELLOWSTONE, by Thomas Moran; acquired by purchase in 1872; transferred to the Department of the Interior in 1950, by provisions of Public Law 603, 81st Congress, 2nd Session, approved July 10, 1950. Painting located in Interior Department Museum.

CHASM of the COLORADO
Painting by Thomas Moran.
Transferred to the Department of the Interior in 1950, now located in the Interior Department Museum.

Courtesy of the Department of Interior   Neg. No. 26896

Neg. No. 26895

GRAND CANYON of the YELLOWSTONE
Painting by Thomas Moran.

Transferred to the Department of Interior in 1950, now located in the Interior Department Museum.

JOSEPH HENRY (first Secretary of the Smithsonian Institution), by Henry Ulke; transferred to the Smithsonian Institution in 1917, by Senate Resolution 334, 64th Congress, 2nd Session, agreed to February 5, 1917.

GENERAL WINFIELD SCOTT, by Edward Troye; acquired by purchase in 1891 (U.S. Stats. at Large, Vol. 26, p. 988) and transferred to the Virginia Military Institute on indefinite loan by Public Resolution #21, 76th Congress, approved June 13, 1939.

BENJAMIN WEST, self portrait; acquired by purchase in 1876 and deposited in the Smithsonian Institution in 1917, by direction of the Chairman of the Joint Committee on the Library, John Sharp Williams.

Courtesy of the Smithsonian Institution   Neg. No. 25970

JOSEPH HENRY, first Secretary of the Smithsonian Institution
Portrait by Henry Ulke.
Location: transferred to the Smithsonian Institution in 1917.

Courtesy of the Smithsonian Institution   Neg. No. 25969

BENJAMIN WEST
Self-portrait.
Location: transferred to the Smithsonian Institution in 1917.

GENERAL WINFIELD SCOTT
Portrait by Edward Troye.
Location: transferred to the Virginia Military Institute in 1939.

Six Statues and Monuments

FREEDOM, Statue of: The original full-sized plaster model of the bronze statue atop the Dome of the United States Capitol by Thomas Crawford, was exhibited in the old Hall of the House, now Statuary Hall, in 1859. It was taken apart and stored in the basement of the Capitol until December 1890, when it was transferred to the Smithsonian Institution by Edward Clark, Architect of the Capitol.

IL PENSEROSO, marble statue by Joseph Mozier. Purchased by the Joint Committee on the Library, December 1872 for $2,000, plus $107.97 for freight and other expenses. Placed on exhibition in the Old Hall of the House of Repre-sentatives. It was transferred to the National Museum, by direction of the Joint Committee on the Library, May 17, 1888.

TECUMSEH, THE DYING—by Chevalier Ferdinand Pettrich. This statue was exhibited in the Rotunda of the Capitol at the time of the funeral of Abraham Lincoln in 1865 and later in the Crypt. By the Act of July 20, 1868 prohibiting the exhibition of works of art in the Capitol not government property, the statue was transferred to the Corcoran Gallery of Art in 1878, where it remained until 1916, when it was transferred to the National Museum.

TRIPOLI OR PEACE MONUMENT—by Charles Micali of Italy and purchased by officers of the United States Navy to memorialize the losses of the Navy at Tripoli. It arrived in Washington, D.C. in 1808. It was erected at the Washington Navy Yard, where it remained until 1831, when it was removed to the West Front of the Capitol. By Act approved June 22, 1860 (U.S. Stats. at large Vol. 12, pg. 83.) the monument was removed from the Capitol to the grounds of the United States Naval Academy at Annapolis, Maryland.

WASHINGTON, GEORGE—Statue modeled by Horatio Greenough in Florence, Italy was acquired by purchase 1833–1836; installed in the Rotunda in 1841 and moved in 1844 to the East Capitol Grounds. In 1908 it was transferred to the Smithsonian Institution under provisions of Public Resolution No. 26, 60th Congress, 1st Session, approved May 30, 1908. On the original pedestal was inscribed "First in War, First in Peace, First in the Hearts of His Countrymen."

WASHINGTON, GEORGE, Statue of: Plaster model by William J. Hubard made from the statue by Antoine Houdon in Richmond, Virginia. This plaster model was in the Capitol in the 1850's but did not become the property of the Government until 1870 when Congress provided $2,000, by Act approved July 15, 1870 to pay the widow of the modeler, Mrs. William Hubard. In accordance with the provisions of Public Law 605, 81st Congress, 2nd Session, approved July 11, 1950 (Senate Joint Resolution 171), the plaster model was transferred to the Smithsonian Institution in 1950, a bronze replica having been presented to the National Statuary Hall Collection by the State of Virginia.

Neg. No. 10421

STATUE OF FREEDOM
Plaster model by Thomas Crawford.
Original bronze statue atop the
Dome of the United States Capitol.
Location: Smithsonian Institution
Washington, D. C.

Courtesy of the Smithsonian Institution
Neg. No. 25972

IL PENSEROSO
Statue by Joseph Mozier.
Location: transferred to the National
Museum in 1888.

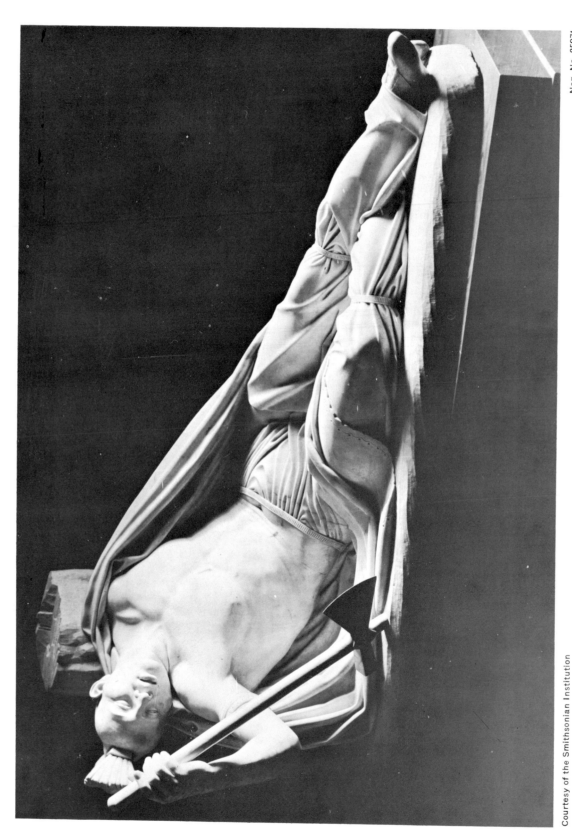

DYING TECUMSEH

Statue by Chevalier Ferdinand Pettrich.

Location: transferred to the National Museum in 1916.

TRIPOLI or PEACE MONUMENT
Executed by Charles Micali of Italy.
Transferred from the Capitol to the grounds of the United States Naval Academy at Annapolis, Maryland.

GEORGE WASHINGTON
Statue by Horatio Greenough.
Transferred from the United States Capitol to the Smithsonian Institution in 1908.

The inscription on the statue base reads:

GEORGE WASHINGTON.

The General Assembly of the Commonwealth
of Virginia have caused this Statue to be erected
as a monument of affection and gratitude to
GEORGE WASHINGTON:
who, uniting to the endowments of the Hero
the virtues of the Patriot, and exerting both
in establishing the Liberties of his Country
has rendered his name dear to his Fellow Citizens,
and given the world an immortal example
of true Glory. Done, in the year of
CHRIST.
One thousand seven hundred and eighty eight,
and in the year of the Commonwealth the twelfth.

GEORGE WASHINGTON
Plaster statue by William J. Hubard, from the original statue by Antoine Houdon in
Richmond, Virginia.
Transferred from the United States Capitol to the Smithsonian
Institution in 1950.

Works of Art Lost in Fires in the United States Capitol

Partial Listing—Records Incomplete

Burning of the United States Capitol—August 24, 1814—War of 1812. The British invaded the City of Washington and took possession of the United States Capitol August 24, 1814. By means of rockets, tar barrels, furniture, books from the Library, paintings and portraits, the structure was soon in flames. Many works of art and valuable manuscript records were lost.

Library of Congress Fire—December 24, 1851.

Model Room Fire—January 3, 1930.

The Library of Congress, located at this date in the United States Capitol, was almost totally destroyed by fire on December 24, 1851. Over three-fifths of the books in the Library were destroyed. In addition, paintings, portraits and busts were lost in these fires:

JOHN ADAMS, portrait by Gilbert Stuart; destroyed in the Library fire of 1851. (Owned by Mr. Phelps of Boston).

JOHN QUINCY ADAMS, bust by Luigi Persico; destroyed in the Library fire of 1851.

JOHN QUINCY ADAMS, portrait by J. Cranch; destroyed in the Library fire of 1851.

MARIE ANTOINETTE, portrait by Madame Vigee Le Brun; thought to be lost in the fire of 1814.

APOLLO, bust or statue by unlisted artist; destroyed in the Library fire of 1851.

SAMUEL BLODGET, JR., Supervisor of Public Buildings; portrait reputed to be by John Trumbull; destroyed in the Model Room fire of 1930.

SIMON BOLIVAR, portrait by unlisted artist; destroyed in the Library fire of 1851.

PIETRO BONANNI, self portrait; destroyed in the Model Room fire of 1930.

CHRISTOPHER COLUMBUS, two portraits by unlisted artists; destroyed in the Library fire of 1851.

CHRISTOPHER COLUMBUS, bust by Giuseppe Ceracchi; destroyed in the Library fire of 1851.

HERNANDO CORTEZ, portrait by unlisted artist; destroyed in the Library fire of 1851.

JUDGE C. D. DRAKE, Chief Justice of the Court of Claims, portrait by Charles Bittinger; destroyed in the Model Room fire of 1930.

JOHN HANSON, portrait by unlisted artist; destroyed in the Library fire of 1851.

F. HAPLER, plaster bust by unlisted artist; destroyed in the Library fire of 1851.

FERDINAND R. HASSLER, bust destroyed in the Library fire of 1851; a gift from his children.

GENERAL ANDREW JACKSON, plaster bust; destroyed in the Library fire of 1851.

THOMAS JEFFERSON, marble bust by Giuseppe Ceracchi; destroyed in the Library fire of 1851.

THOMAS JEFFERSON, portrait by Gilbert Stuart; destroyed in the Library fire of 1851. (Owned by Mr. Phelps of Boston).

THOMAS JEFFERSON, statue by unlisted artist; destroyed in the Library fire of 1851.

WILLIAM JOHNSON, portrait by unlisted artist; destroyed in the Library fire of 1851.

BARON DE KALB, portrait by unlisted artist; destroyed in the Library fire of 1851.

MARQUIS DE LAFAYETTE, marble bust by David d'Angers; destroyed in the Library fire of 1851.

LIBERTY AND THE EAGLE, statue by Giuseppe Franzoni; destroyed in the fire of 1814.

LOUIS XVI, portrait by Madame Vigee Le Brun; thought to be destroyed in the fire of 1814.

JAMES MADISON, bust (medallion); destroyed in the Library fire of 1851.

JAMES MADISON, portrait by Gilbert Stuart; destroyed in the Library fire of 1851. (Owned by Mr. Phelps of Boston).

JOHN MARSHALL, Chief Justice, plaster bust; destroyed in the Library fire of 1851.

JAMES MONROE, portrait by Gilbert Stuart; destroyed in the Library fire of 1851. (Owned by Mr. Phelps of Boston).

GOVERNOR MOULTRIE, plaster bust by Col. J. S. Cogdell; destroyed in the Library fire of 1851.

OGDALL, plaster bust; destroyed in the Library fire of 1851.

PEYTON RANDOLPH, portrait by unlisted artist; destroyed in the Library fire of 1851.

ZACHARY TAYLOR, marble bust by unlisted artist; destroyed in the Library fire of 1851.

AMERICUS VESPUCIUS, bust by Giuseppe Cerracchi; destroyed in the Library fire of 1851.

BARON VON STEUBEN, portrait by Pyne; destroyed in the Library fire of 1851.

GEORGE WASHINGTON, bust by Giuseppe Cerracchi; destroyed in the Library fire of 1851.

GEORGE WASHINGTON, bronze bust by David d'Angers; destroyed in the Library fire of 1851.

GEORGE WASHINGTON, portrait by Gilbert Stuart; destroyed in the Library fire of 1851. (Owned by Mr. Phelps of Boston).

L. WOODBURY, plaster bust; destroyed in the Library fire of 1851.

MEDALS, about 1200 medals, damaged by the Library fire of 1851, but not destroyed, were authorized by the Joint Committee on the Library to be presented by the Librarian to the Smithsonian Institution July 19, 1861.

(no illustrations)

Works of Art Which Are Not Carried in the Records of the Architect of the Capitol as a Part of the Capitol Art Collection

(NO ILLUSTRATIONS)

The Joint Committee on the Library has not acted towards acceptance of these works of art—some gifts, some left by owners who cannot be located, some for which the records are incomplete and some works which cannot now be located.

Busts

THEODORE E. BURTON, a Representative and a Senator from Ohio. Plaster bust by Elizabeth Kidder Sparrow. Gift from the artist. Located in Room 1302, Public Works Committee, House of Representatives.

JAMES F. BYRNES, a Representative and Senator from South Carolina. Marble bust by Bryant Baker, presented to the Joint Committee on the Library in April 1948 by friends of Mr. Byrnes in South Carolina. This bust has not been accepted and is at present stored in the Office of the Architect of the Capitol.

Plaster bust, *subject and artist unknown*. (Sometimes referred to as Columbus). Located in the Office of the Architect of the Capitol, HT–6.

ABRAHAM LINCOLN, a Representative from Illinois and a President of the United States. Bronze bust by unknown artist, formerly located in the Senate Marble Room. Gift of Col. A. DeGroot. Placed in the Capitol in 1871. Present location unknown.

THOMAS J. WALSH, a Senator from Montana. Plaster bust by Elizabeth Kidder Sparrow. Gift from the artist. Formerly located in the Senate Office Building; present location unknown.

Painting

UNITED STATES CAPITOL, WEST FRONT. Presented by John C. Stevens in 1946 to the United States Government, Office of the Architect of the Capitol. Located in the Architect's Office, SB–16.

Portraits

AGASSIZ, American naturalist. Portrait by Henry Ulke. Purchased February 7, 1877. Present location unknown.

HENRY FOUNTAIN ASHURST, a Senator from Arizona. Portrait painted by Azadia in 1941. It was hung in Room S–212, April 1964. This portrait is the personal property of Senator Carl Hayden, having been presented to him by Mrs. Louise Cromwell MacArthur Heiberg.

HAROLD R. BECKLEY, former Superintendent of the Senate Press Gallery. Enlarged photograph tinted in oil by Gladys A. Kazigian; located in the Press Room of the New Senate Office Building. This portrait was presented by the Correspondents' Committee.

WILLIAM JENNINGS BRYAN, a Representative from Nebraska. Portrait by Michel Jacobs; located in the office of Congressman Dorn of South Carolina, Room 330, Cannon House Office Building.

JOSEPH G. CANNON, former Speaker of the House of Representatives. Portrait by Michel Jacobs; located in the Superintendent's Office, Personnel, Room 260, Cannon House Office Building.

JOSEPH G. CANNON, former Speaker of the House of Representatives. Portrait by George Burroughs Torrey; located in the Architect's Storeroom.

CHAMP CLARK, former Speaker of the House of Representatives. Portrait by Michel Jacobs; located in the office of the late Honorable Clarence Cannon of Missouri, Room 1712, Longworth House Office Building.

CHARLES A. EATON, Representative from New Jersey. Portrait formerly located in the office of Congressman Eaton, House wing of the Capitol. This portrait is the personal property of Congressman Eaton, having been presented to him in 1951.

CHARLES E. FAIRMAN, former Art Curator of the Capitol and Chief Clerk of the Office of the Architect of the Capitol. Portrait by Nicholas R. Brewer; located in the Office of the Architect of the Capitol; Room SB–15 a gift from Mr. Fairman.

THOMAS HENDRICKS, a Representative and Senator from Indiana and a Vice President of the United States. Portrait by unknown artist. In 1910, it was located in the Senate Judiciary Committee Room; present location unknown.

DAVID LAUPHEIMER, founder of the Page Boys School. Portrait by unknown artist. Presented to the Page Boys School in 1953; present location unknown.

ABRAHAM LINCOLN, a Representative from Illinois and a President of the United States. Portrait by Boris B. Gordon; located in the Office of the Secretary of the Senate. This portrait was placed in the Office of the Secretary of the Senate in 1946 with the consent of the chairman of the Joint Committee on the Library, in order that it might be available for view by the committee, for consideration for purchase. To date, no action has been taken with respect to its acquisition.

ABRAHAM LINCOLN, a Representative from Illinois and a President of the United States. Portrait by Griswold Tyng, formerly located in Room S–229, now in Room S–113, Senators' Private Dining Room. This portrait was presented by the family of the late Senator Kenneth S. Wherry in January 1952 as a gift to "Future Senate Republican Floor Leaders."

HENRY CABOT LODGE, a Representative and Senator from Massachusetts. Portrait by Boris Gordon. Stored in the Senate Janitor's Office on the Senate Terrace.

JOHN T. MORGAN, a Senator from Alabama and chairman of the Senate Committee on Foreign Relations at the time of his death in 1907. Portrait by Carl Gutherz. The records of the Architect of the Capitol indicate that this portrait is the property of the daughter of the late Senator Morgan. The portrait was offered by his daughter to the Joint Committee on the Library in 1910, but no action of acceptance was ever taken. The portrait has, however, remained in the Capitol since 1910, its return never having been requested. It is presently located in Room S–339 in the Capitol.

JUSTIN MORRILL, a Representative and Senator from Vermont. Portrait by Carl Gutherz; formerly located in the office of Senator Warren R. Austin; now stored in the Senate Janitor's Office.

FRANKLIN DELANO ROOSEVELT, former President of the United States. Portrait by unknown artist. Presented by the National Italian American Civic League, 1937; in storage in the Office of the Architect of the Capitol. No record available as to whom this portrait was presented.

MORRIS SHEPPARD, a Representative and a Senator from Texas. Portrait by B. Godwin, 1939. Located in the Architect's Storeroom. No record available on this portrait.

ROBERT A. TAFT, a Senator from Ohio. Portrait painted by Rudolph Bernatschke in 1953; located in the office of the Senate Minority Leader. The portrait was presented by the artist June 17, 1959 to be hung in the office of the Republican Senate Floor Leader in the Capitol, Room S–230.

HARRY S. TRUMAN, a Senator from Missouri, a Vice President, and a President of the United States. Portrait by Greta Kempton; located in Room S–310, Office of the Majority Whip in the Capitol, Senate side. No information available to the Architect of the Capitol as to the ownership of this portrait.

HARRY S. TRUMAN, a Senator from Missouri, a Vice President, and a President of the United States. Photographic reproduction in color by Greta Kempton. Located in Room S–318 in the Capitol. A gift to the Senate Democratic Policy Committee.

NICHOLAS VAN DYKE, JR., a Senator from Delaware. Portrait by Jefferson D. Chalfant. The records of the Architect of the Capitol indicate that this portrait was presented to the Senate in 1914 by the great granddaughters of the late Senator Van Dyke, and although received by the Joint Committee on the Library, was never accepted by that committee. Its present ownership is doubtful. The portrait has remained in the Capitol since 1914, and its return has never been requested. It is presently located in the Office of the Senate Majority Leader, S–210.

GEORGE WASHINGTON, President of the United States. Colored lithograph located in Room S–114 (Senators' Private Dining Room) in the Capitol.

DANIEL WEBSTER, a Representative from New Hampshire and a Representative and a Senator from Massachusetts. Portrait painted by Francis H. Cumberland in 1961; hung in March 1963 in Room S–146, Senate Appropriations Committee Hearing Room. This portrait was a gift of the artist. Records not completed.

Statues aud Statuettes

UNCLE SAM '76, plaster statuette reputed to have been executed by Horatio Stone. Located in the Office of the Architect of the Capitol. Records incomplete.

Paintings and Portraits on Indefinite Loan to the Capitol

(NO ILLUSTRATIONS)

Paintings—Not the Property of the Government

CONSTITUTION, UNITED STATES FRIGATE ESCAPING FROM THE BRITISH FLEET IN 1812, by F. Mullen. This painting is located in the Office of the Clerk of the House of Representatives, in the Extension of the Capitol. It had been located since 1932 in his former office near Statuary Hall. Information furnished by the Clerk of the House indicates that the painting is the property of the Navy Department, having been originally loaned to the Senate Committee on Naval Affairs.

Paintings—From the Department of Defense To the Senate Committee on Armed Services

ROOM 212, SENATE OFFICE BUILDING

These five paintings are on loan to the Senate Armed Services Committee from the Department of Defense, and have been hanging in the Committee rooms since 1947.

CAMOUFLAGED 75MM HOWITZER, by Olin Dows.
LUNCH TIME NEAR MIGNANO, by Edward A. Reep.
"MEAT WAGON" POOL, by Howard Baer.
102ND MECHANIZED CAVALRY PREPARING TO MOVE OUT, by Olin Dows.
SMOKE SCREEN AT ANZIO BEACHHEAD, by Rudolph Von Ripper.

Paintings—From the Department of Defense To the Senate Committee on Appropriations

ROOM S-126, UNITED STATES CAPITOL

ARTILLERY POSITIONS ABOVE LOIANO, by T/Sgt. Savo Radulovich.
CHINESE COOLIES UNLOADING AMMUNITION AT KWEILI'N, by T/Sgt. Samuel D. Smith; loaned in 1946

FIGHTER PLANE MAINTENANCE, by Beaugureau.
TASK FORCE OF TWO NAVIES, by Commander Dwight Sheplar, U.S.N.R.
TRAINING FOR THE 2ND FRONT, by T/Sgt. Stephen Olin Dows.

Portraits—Not the Property of the Government

LINCOLN AND HIS SON TAD, by Franklin Courter; on idenfinite loan from the National Gallery of Art; located in Room S-231, Office of the Senate Minority Leader.
FRANKLIN DELANO ROOSEVELT, by H. S. Hubbell, painted in 1935; on indefinite loan from the Smithsonian Institution, Fine Arts Section; located in Room S-212.
DANIEL WEBSTER, by James R. Lambdin; on indefinite loan from the National Gallery of Art; located in Room S-239.

Paintings—Not the Property of the Government

These three paintings are located in Room S-310, Office of the Senate Majority Whip. No information available to the Architect of the Capitol as to the ownership of these paintings.

BATTLE OF TARAWA, by Tom Lovell
BATTLESHIP, by Jack Coggins
SPIRIT OF ST. LOUIS, by Cinar Monroe

Paintings—Returned to the War Department

These three paintings are the property of the War Department and were on loan to the Senate Committee on Appropriations from 1946 to 1961.

They were located in the committee's room, S–126 in the Capitol, where they were placed in 1946 at the time changes and improvements were made in that room. They were returned to the War Department (Defense Department) in 1961.

AMERICAN PLANES OVER THE ENGLISH COUNTRYSIDE, by Sgt. Harrison Standley, water color painting.

THE LIGHTNINGS FORM UP, by Major John Laualle, A.C., water color painting.

THE WAY BACK, by Lawrence Beall Smith, oil painting.

Paintings—Private Owership

U.S.S. CONSTITUTION—OLD IRONSIDES, by N. W. Canter, April 4, 1934. This painting is located in Room H–204 in the Capitol, occupied by the Speaker of the House of Representatives. It is the personal property of the Speaker, John W. McCormack.

Portraits Carried in 1952 Compilation as Works of Art Not Government Property

ALBEN W. BARKLEY, mosaic portrait; formerly located in the Vice President's private office; removed from the Capitol in 1956 and sent to Kentucky by the family of Mr. Barkley.

LESLIE BIFFLE, portrait by C. J. Fox; formerly located in the Office of the Secretary of the Senate. This portrait is the personal property of Mr. Biffle, former Secretary of the Senate, and was removed from the Capitol in 1958 by Mr. Biffle.

HARRY S. TRUMAN, portrait by Jay Wesley Jacobs; located in the Office of the Secretary of the Senate. This portrait was loaned to Mr. Biffle, former Secretary of the Senate, in 1945. It was removed from the Capitol by Mr. Biffle and returned to its owner.

WOODROW WILSON, portrait by J. W. Gunther; located in the Office of the Speaker of the House of Representatives. This portrait was the personal property of the late Speaker Rayburn and is now located in the Sam Rayburn Foundation Library, Bonham, Texas.

Portraits of Chairmen of Committees—Not Government Property

SHELBY M. CULLOM, portrait by August Benziger. Formerly located in the room of the Senate Committee on Foreign Relations. Returned to the owner in Illinois in 1948 at the direction of the Chairman of the Senate Committee on Rules.

Index

405

416

421

422

U.S. GOVERNMENT PRINTING OFFICE: 1965   O—39-071

UNITED STATES CAPITOL, West Front

Neg. No. 10605